M...
TO BE FREE

A Flight North on the Underground Railroad

JOANNA HALPERT KRAUS

Resource Material
Cecily O'Neill

Series Consultant
Cecily O'Neill

COLLINS
EDUCATIONAL

Copyright © 1990 playscript Joanna Halpert Kraus;
resource material Cecily O'Neill

Originally published by New Plays Incorporated,
1967

ISBN 0 00 330240 7

Acknowledgments
The following permissions to reproduce material are
gratefully acknowledged:
Harvard University Press for the extracts on pages
viii, 46 and 65 from *Narrative of the Life of Frederick
Douglass*, edited by Benjamin Quarles, 1960; Puffin
Books for the extracts on pages 43, 44 and 58 and the
song 'We raise the wheat' on page 50 from *To Be a
Slave* by Julius Lester, 1973; Harold Ober Associates
Inc for the poem 'Southern Mansion' on page 49 from
Personals, edited by Paul Breman, 1973; Planetary-
Nom (London) for the verse from 'Strange Fruit' by
Lewis Allan, sung by Billie Holiday on *Lady Sings the
Blues*, Verve 3113–109, Polydor, on page 50; Random
House for the story 'The People Could Fly' on pages
52–55 from *The People Could Fly: American Black
Folktales*, told by Virginia Hamilton, 1986; Clarke,
Irwin and Company for the extract on page 71 from
Underground to Canada by Barbara Smucker, 1977;
Random House for part of 'Lennox Avenue Mural' by
Langston Hughes on page 74 from *The Panther and
the Lash: Poems of Our Time* by Langston Hughes,
1961; The Estate of Martin Luther King Jr for
extracts from his speeches on pages 75 and 77,
reprinted by permission of Harper and Row
Publishers and Joan Daves; Virago Press for the
extract from 'Still I Rise' by Maya Angelou on page 78

Illustrations
Mary Evans Picture Library: pages 41, 42, 44, 45 and
49
Hulton-Deutsch Collection: pages 73 and 77
Peter Newark's American Pictures: pages x and 65
Popperfoto: page 75
It has not been possible to trace the owner of the
copyright of the illustration used on the cover. We
should be glad to hear from anyone with knowledge of
ownership.

Design by Carla Turchini
Typeset by Northern Phototypesetting Co. Ltd., Bolton
Printed by Bell and Bain Ltd., Glasgow

CONTENTS

BACKGROUND TO THE PLAY

SLAVERY

In the 17th century, the developing colonies of the 'New World'
were desperate for labour. In America, the southern states
needed people to work on the rice, sugar and cotton plantations.
Slave traders brought hundreds of thousands of Africans who
had been tricked, captured or sold into slavery across the
Atlantic. They were carried in specially designed slave ships,
chained up below deck in spaces not much bigger than coffins.
Many died of disease or suffocation, and were thrown overboard.
Others resisted and were killed, or threw themselves into the sea

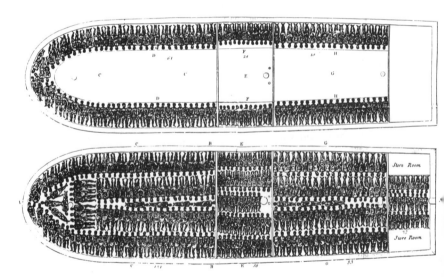

A plan of a slave ship

rather than face a life of slavery. Perhaps as many as one in three of these prisoners died during the crossing.

The profits of this trade were immense, and many European countries, including Britain, were involved. British ships set out from Bristol and Liverpool, carrying cargoes like brandy and guns to the ports of West Africa. In exchange, they took on board men, women and children who had been captured on slave raids

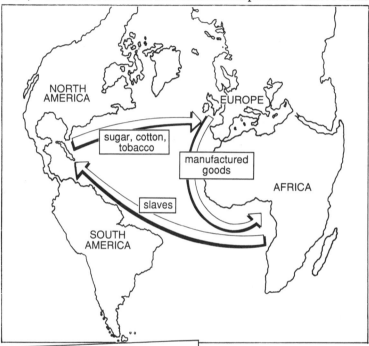

The 'triangular trade'

There is not a brick in the city but what is cemented with the blood of a slave. Sumptuous mansions, luxurious living, liveried menials, were the produce of the wealth made from the sufferings and groans of the slaves bought and sold by the Bristol merchants.

J F Nicholls and J Taylor, two 19th century Bristol historians

Ships sailed from the 'mother country' with goods which they exchanged on the west coast of Africa for slaves. The slaves were taken across the Atlantic and sold in the West Indies, North and South America, to work on the plantations. The same ships were then loaded with raw materials, food and luxuries from the plantations, which were taken back and sold in the 'mother country'.

into the heart of the African continent. By 1800, between ten and fifteen million people had been transported to the Americas as slaves.

When the slave ships arrived in America, the survivors of that terrible journey were sold in slave auctions, and taken away to work, usually on the plantations. These were large farms in the South, whose main crop was cotton. The slaves were regarded as the property of their owners, and spent their whole lives working long hours in the fields or in the houses of the white people for no wages. In the late 18th century, one slave owner boasted that he made nearly $300 a year from the labour of one of his slaves who cost him only $12 in keep. The only way a slave could leave a master was by being sold to another owner.

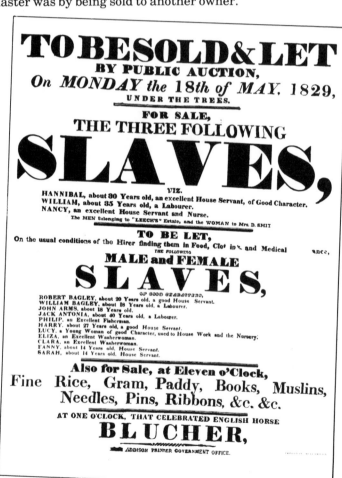

Abolitionists

Slavery did not exist in the northern states and many people wanted to abolish slavery throughout the country. These people, who worked to abolish slavery and the slave trade, were called abolitionists.

Some of the abolitionists formed a secret network to help runaway slaves escape to freedom in the North. No one knows where the name originally came from, but the network of escape routes began to be called the Underground Railroad. The abolitionists used the language of the real railroad to confuse their enemies. They called themselves 'conductors'; safe houses and hiding-places were known as 'stations' on the 'railroad'; and the runaway slaves were the 'passengers'. Thousands of slaves reached freedom on the invisible tracks of this 'railroad'. Many of the 'conductors' showed great courage and endurance, facing prison, heavy fines and, in the case of ex-slaves who went back to the South to help others escape, the real danger of capture and a return to slavery.

Harriet Tubman was one of the most heroic and determined of the conductors on the Underground Railroad, but there were many others, black and white, slaves and free, who risked their lives and liberty to bring others to freedom. Among the most courageous were Frederick Douglass, a runaway slave who became a well-known lecturer, statesman, newspaper editor and writer against slavery; Josiah Henson, at first a trusted slave and overseer, but who finally escaped to Canada with many others; Sojourner Truth, born a slave, who became famous for her inspired speeches about the evils of slavery and discrimination against women; John Brown, the white, sixty-year-old leader of an uprising of slaves in the South, who was captured by the militia and hanged, and who is commemorated in the song 'John Brown's body lies a mouldering in the grave'.

In his last statement, before he was hanged, John Brown wrote:

I, John Brown, am quite certain that the crimes of this guilty land will never be purged away but with blood.

Frederick Douglass, a slave, was sent to work in Baltimore as a servant and labourer in the shipyard. He taught himself to read and write and in 1838 escaped to the North. In his autobiography, Narrative of the Life of Frederick Douglass, *he remembered his thoughts, as a child, about being a slave:*

Why am I a slave? Why are some people slaves and others masters? Was there ever a time when this was not so? How did the relation commence?

Once, however, engaged in the inquiry, I was not very long in finding out the true solution of the matter. It was not colour, but crime, not God, but man, that afforded the true explanation of the existence of slavery; nor was I long in finding out another important truth: that is, what man can make, man can unmake ...

For the black women abolitionists, there were many hurdles to face – as abolitionists in a slave-owning society, as black people among white reformers, and as women in a movement dominated by men. When Sojourner Truth rose to speak at a convention in New York in 1853, the crowd was hostile. She said:

I know that it feels a kind o' hissin' and ticklin' like to see a coloured woman get up and tell you about things, and Women's Rights. We have all been thrown down so low that nobody thought we'd ever get up again; but ... we will come up again, and now I'm here ... we'll have our rights; see if we don't; and you can't stop us from them; see if you can. You may hiss as much as you like, but it is comin' ... I am sittin' among you to watch; and every once in awhile I will come out and tell you what time of night it is ...

Many Quakers were noted abolitionists, including Thomas Garrett who appears in the play. He made no secret of his determination to help as many runaway slaves as possible, and collaborated with Harriet Tubman. He suffered heavy fines and constant hostility for his part in helping more than 2,000 slaves to freedom, but never gave up the struggle.

Other Quakers who were firmly opposed to slavery were Levi Coffin and his wife Catherine, who helped so many runaways that their home was known as the Grand Central Station of the Underground Railroad. Harriet Beecher Stowe also hid many fleeing slaves, and her book, *Uncle Tom's Cabin*, although later criticised for what was seen as its distorted view of slave life, was influential in rallying huge numbers of people to the anti-slavery cause. Although at this time women were expected to remain at home as housewives and mothers, many defied their families and friends to become active in the abolitionist movement. Men and women of many different religions and races, some of whom are famous, and many hundreds more whose names are long forgotten, were united in their efforts to fight against the inhumanity of slavery.

Emancipation

Gradually, the tide of public opinion began to turn against slave holders. The smouldering differences between the northern and southern states came to a head when Abraham Lincoln, who was opposed to slavery, was elected President of the United States in 1860. The Civil War, which became almost inevitable, broke out in 1861 and was fought to save the Union. There could, however, be no union without emancipation – that is, freedom for the slaves. In 1865, the northern armies of the Union defeated the southern forces – the Confederacy – and slavery in the United States was officially at an end. But the wounds inflicted by slavery took a long time to heal. Even a hundred years after the abolition of slavery, the scars are still visible. To be black in America has meant a constant struggle against prejudice, segregation, poverty of opportunity and exclusion from the mainstream of American life.

It was not until the flowering of the civil rights movement in the 1960s, led by Martin Luther King, that black people were finally included in the democratic process begun a century earlier. But in 1968, Martin Luther King was assassinated. The struggle for equality – as well as liberty – goes on.

HARRIET TUBMAN

Harriet Tubman

Harriet Tubman was born on a cotton plantation in Maryland in 1820, one of a family of eleven children. Like other slave children, she worked long hours in the cotton fields. One day, when she was about fifteen, she tried to prevent an overseer whipping a slave. In a rage, the man seized the nearest thing to hand, a two-pound iron weight, and flung it straight at Harriet. It struck her on the head and knocked her senseless. She lay unconscious for many days and carried the scar from the blow for the rest of her life.

When she was in her twenties, the plantation was sold, and the new owner planned to sell off the slaves. Harriet decided to run away. She knew that there was no slavery in the northern states, and guided by the North Star, she made the painful and dangerous journey northwards to freedom. At last, in spite of the fearful dangers of the journey – swamps, raging rivers, armed patrols on horseback, bloodhounds and posters offering rewards for runaway slaves – she crossed into Pennsylvania. Although she was free, she felt like a stranger in a strange land.

In Philadelphia, the biggest city in Pennsylvania, she found work as a cook in a boarding house and saved hard – but she could not forget the people she had left behind in bondage. 'I saw their tears' she said, 'and heard their cries. I would have given every drop of my blood to free them.'

Her own freedom was not enough, and she went back to the South again and again to bring other slaves to liberty. Among those she rescued were her own brothers and sisters, and even her elderly parents, who were too old to make the journey on foot. She bought a horse and cart, hid them under a load of straw, and drove them to safety.

In 1850, the government passed the Fugitive Slave Act. This meant that people in the free northern states could be forced to return runaway slaves to their owners. Anyone caught helping a slave to escape could be sent to prison. Slave owners hired spies and hunters to find and bring back their missing slaves, and sometimes even those who were free and could be captured and delivered to a life of slavery in the South.

It was clear to Harriet Tubman that there was no safety anywhere in the United States for runaway slaves. Now she had to lead them all the way to Canada, where they would be on the soil of the British Empire and where slavery had been outlawed. The journey to Canada was very long – over 500 miles – but many people were brought safely from the South to freedom on the Underground Railroad. The signal to any escaping slave was either a birdcall in the darkness or the singing sound of a spiritual like 'Go down, Moses'. Harriet, often in disguise, brought remedies for illnesses, poppy seeds to make babies sleep, and a gun to make sure that no one thought of turning back or betraying the runaways. She would turn her loaded gun on any frightened or reluctant runaway and offer them a choice: 'You can go on, or you can die.'

She described the feelings which drove her on in this way:

> *There was one of two things I had a right to, liberty or death; if I could not have one, I would have the other; for no man should take me alive ...*

Harriet had many friends and helpers along the way, and made contact with them by secret signs, passwords and beacons. Her most important friend was the Quaker Thomas Garrett, who lived in Wilmington, Delaware, and who is one of the characters in the play. He helped hundreds of runaway slaves, and was often fined thousands of dollars for breaking the law.

By the time Harriet made her last journey to free the slaves, there was a reward offered for her capture of $40,000 – a huge sum in those days. In spite of the promise of riches, no one ever betrayed her.

When the Civil War broke out between the free northern states and the slave-owning southern states, Harriet worked for the northern army – first as a cook and then as a nurse. After two years of war, she was given work as a spy for the Union army. She explored rivers, joined in the fighting and persuaded slaves on defeated plantations to join the Union army. On one expedition, she freed 750 slaves. After the war, Harriet settled down with her parents in a little house in the state of New York. She continued throughout her life, however, to speak out and to campaign against injustices – injustices against black people, women, the poor ...

With a small army pension, she was able to buy some land, provide for her family and help the poor. She spent the final years of her life trying to establish the John Brown Home for the Aged – named after the man hanged for his part in an uprising of slaves.

A woman writer called Sarah Bradford persuaded Harriet to tell her own story. It was published in 1886 and called *Harriet, the Moses of Her People*. Harriet lived to the age of ninety-three. Her home is now a museum, keeping fresh the memory of her courage. A plaque on the wall of her house reads:

> *In memory of Harriet Tubman, called the Moses of her people. With rare courage she led over five hundred black people from slavery to freedom and rendered invaluable service as nurse and spy in the war. She braved every danger and overcame every obstacle. With all she possessed, extraordinary foresight and judgment so that she could truthfully say 'On my Underground Railroad I never ran my train off the track and I never lost a passenger'.*

Runagate, Runagate

Rises from their anguish and their power,

Harriet Tubman,

woman of earth, whipscarred,
a summoning, a shining

Mean to be free

> And this was the way of it, brethren brethren,
> way we journeyed from Can't to Can.
> Moon so bright and no place to hide,
> the cry up and the paterollers riding,
> hound dogs belling in bladed air.
> And fear starts a-murbling, Never make it,
> we'll never make it. *Hush that now,*
> and she's turned upon us, levelled pistol
> glinting in the moonlight:
> Dead folks can't jaybird-talk, she says;
> you keep on going now or die, she says.

Wanted Harriet Tubman alias The General
alias Moses Stealer of Slaves

In league with Garrison Alcott Emerson
Garrett Douglass Thoreau John Brown

Armed and known to be Dangerous

Wanted Reward Dead or Alive

> Tell me, Ezekiel, oh tell me do you see
> mailed Jehovah coming to deliver me?

Hoot-owl calling in the ghosted air,
five times calling to the hands in the air.
Shadow of a face in the scary leaves,
shadow of a voice in the talking leaves:

> Come ride-a my train

> *Oh that train, ghost-story train*
> *through swamp and savanna movering movering,*
> *over trestles of dew, through caves of the wish,*
> *Midnight Special on a sabre track movering movering*
> first stop Mercy and the last Hallelujah.

> Come ride-a my train

> Mean mean mean to be free.

The Characters

HEDY – aged nine

TOM – aged eleven

MISS NANCY – wife of the owner of the Tidewater, a Maryland plantation. She is quick-tempered, self-centred and determined to have her own way on all plantation matters.

MOSES – (Harriet Tubman), a former slave in her mid-thirties, short and plain in appearance. Now she is a conductor on the Underground Railroad. She is deeply religious.

LINDA – aged seventeen, formerly a lady's maid on a plantation. She is delicate and spoiled.

JOE – in his mid-thirties; a former overseer of a plantation. He is handsome, hardworking and has an innate sense of dignity.

THOMAS GARRETT
SARAH GARRETT } devout Quakers whose house has become one of the stops on the Underground Railroad

TWO MEN – pursuers of fugitive slaves

TWO BRICKLAYERS

POLICEMAN

OLIVER JOHNSON – head of the Anti-Slavery Office in New York City

RAILROAD CONDUCTOR

MEAN TO BE FREE

Act One
SCENE ONE

*Tidewater, a Maryland plantation, just before the Civil War, 1857. A backdrop, if used, would suggest fields of hay and stacked cornfields. On stage there is a windowless log cabin, its chinks filled with mud, which serves as the laundry cabin. The entrance to it is merely an opening in the wall. Inside there are huge washtubs, scrubbing boards, and so on. It is an autumn, Saturday afternoon. **Hedy**, aged nine, drags a heavy washtub over to a pile of sheets. She kneels and begins the laborious chore of scrubbing the sheets clean.*

TOM *enters, terrified. He sinks on the floor beside **Hedy**. His shirt is bloody and torn. He is half crying* Hedy!

HEDY Tom! *Stops her work* What happened?

TOM Hedy, it hurts bad. You gotta help me. He used the whip.

HEDY How many times?

TOM Plenty!

HEDY *lifts his shirt gingerly* Here, I'll wash it off for you.

During the next few speeches, she cleans the wound.

Tom, you get into any more trouble and they're gonna sell you down river . . . tie your hands and feet to a big rope, the way they did Old Jim. Who beat you?

TOM Master Ed.

HEDY Master Ed! What'd you do?

TOM All I done was take a peach. It was there hangin' on the bough. Big and juicy. Just waitin' to be 'et. I was hungry. Real hungry. There it was. Wasn't anyone around. Oh, I know I shouldn't have done it.

1

HEDY *shocked* You mean that peach tree near the big house window? *Tom nods* But that's Miss Nancy's own tree. She planted it herself. I heard Mama say so.

TOM It was quiet. All the white folks were having lunch. I could smell the food. Didn't think no one could see me. But Miss Nancy, she looked out the window and screamed, 'Robber! Robber!'. And Master Ed came out with his whip . . . with his whip, Hedy.

HEDY Mama told you not to go near the big house. And you shouldn't steal, Tom. Mama told you that. *Hedy finishes wiping the wound* Does it feel better, Tom?

TOM *nods* Thanks, Hedy. *Miss Nancy sweeps in. Tom moves away. Hedy conceals the cloth.*

MISS NANCY I thought I heard a **boy's** voice down here. A familiar boy's voice. *To Hedy* Looks to me like there's plenty of work to do, Hedy. And talking doesn't get it done.

HEDY Yes, Miss Nancy.

Hedy begins scrubbing again.

MISS NANCY to *Tom* So this is the way you repay Master Ed for feeding and clothing you year after year. First, you steal. Now, you stop Hedy from doing her work. You should be ashamed of yourself. *Tom doesn't answer* But I can see you're not. Well, I'll see to it, Tom, that you get another lesson from Master Ed, one you won't forget so easily! *Her anger mounts* A boy like you should be sold! *Pause, says to herself* I'll tell him this afternoon. *To Hedy* Hedy, remember those sheets have to dry in the **sunlight.** You'll have to work a lot faster than you are now. Meanwhile, Tom, get a wash-basin and help your sister until I get back. You've made her lose enough time already.

Miss Nancy exits. Hedy gets a washbasin for Tom.

HEDY Oh, Tom. **Sold!** Then, we'd never ever see you again. She couldn't mean that. Maybe if you work real hard this afternoon and help me finish, she'll forget about talkin' to Master Ed.

TOM No, Hedy. She ain't the kind to forget. And I ain't doin' no laundry either. That's women's work. Miss Nancy knows no man does that kind of work. She knows that, but she told me to do it, just the same. She's just a . . .

HEDY   **Sh-h-h**, Tom! She might come back and hear you!

Sound of whippoorwill.

TOM   *excited*   Hedy, do you know what that is?

HEDY   Sure. A bird down by the river.

MISS NANCY   *offstage*   Hedy, I better not find you talking instead of washing.

Hedy quickly continues to scrub the sheets.

HEDY   C'mon, Tom. Won't you help me finish?

TOM   *looks around to make sure they're alone*   That's a whippoorwill, Hedy.

HEDY   *scared*   Mama says that sound means death, 'cause a whippoorwill doesn't ever sing down by the river.

TOM   That sound ain't no bird, Hedy.   *Whispers* That's Moses calling.

HEDY   Who? Moses! Moses in the Bible. Mama taught me that. You're just trying to fool me. Moses lived some hundred and thousands of years ago.

TOM   Not that one, Hedy. And don't say the name so loud. She's a woman livin' now. And she takes people North, underground, and when they come up, they're all free and safe and happy.

HEDY   You're crazy, Tom.

TOM   No, I ain't. Listen, Hedy.   *Comes close to **Hedy** to tell her the amazing tale*   I hear the old men talking, late at night. They say Moses is tall, tallest woman in the world. They say she can see things a l-o-n-g way off, even in the dark, just like a bat. They say she can run faster than rabbits, climb trees like a possum, jump over fences, and fly over streams . . . and that she can hear a patroller sneeze twenty miles away. There's a price on her head . . . but ain't no one can catch her.   *Sound of whippoorwill.* ***Tom** gets the idea*   And Hedy . . . listen, Hedy, I'm gonna run away with her . . . tonight!

HEDY   *looks around to see if they were overheard*   Tom, if you run away, they'll send the dogs after you and they'll find you and eat you.

TOM   They won't catch me. Not with Moses.

HEDY   But Master Ed says the people up North fatten up runaway slaves and then they eat them.

TOM   He just says that to keep us all from runnin' away. Hedy, do you want to scrub sheets all your life?   *Hedy shakes her head*   Then, come with me. We could make it together.

HEDY   *looks around again*   Ain't it dangerous Tom, to run away? Besides there's Mama and Papa. Anyway, how you gonna get past, Miss Nancy? She'll be back any minute.

TOM   If they're gonna sell me anyway, Hedy, I ain't got nothin' to lose. If they sell me down river, I'll never get away . . . ever. Now's my only chance.   *Tries to persuade her*   Hedy . . . Hedy, don't you want to make Mama and Papa proud of you? Do somethin' beside scrubbin' sheets?

HEDY   *gently*   Oh, Tom, what could I do?

TOM   You could go to school, Hedy. And then you could send Mama and Papa a letter and tell 'em we're fine. And then . . .

HEDY   *interrupts, laughing*   They can't read, and we can't write. Who you foolin'?

TOM   But we could learn. Oh, Hedy, come with me. Up North all the children go to school . . . girls too.   *Sound of whippoorwill.* ***Tom*** *tries to persuade* ***Hedy***   Hedy, it's Saturday. That's the day Moses always starts. They can't print no poster about us on a Sunday, so we'd get at least one day's start.   *Convincing her*   And Hedy, when we're free, then we could help Mama and Papa and we could all have a nice little house together.

She puts the sheets down thoughtfully.

HEDY   *rises*   Could we really help Mama and Papa come North? Really? And all have a nice house together?

TOM   *confident*   Sure we can. Besides there'll be people up there to help us.

HEDY   And could I really learn to read and write, Tom?

TOM   Sure you could, Hedy. But you'll never get a chance to learn down here.   *Hedy stands uncertainly*   Hedy . . . Hedy, if you don't come with me,

4

now, I might never see you. Never! Never again! **Tom** *crosses to entrance to see if* **Miss Nancy** *is in sight.* *Whispers* Hedy, now's my chance. Miss Nancy's just gone inside the big house. I gotta go now. If they see me goin' I'm as good as dead.

Tom *starts out.*

HEDY Wait. Wait for me, Tom. I'm comin' too.
    Softly Goodbye, old sheets. Goodbye, forever!

TOM Quick, Hedy. **Now!**

Tom *grabs her hand. The curtains close.*

The escape is choreographed. Their movements are tense, punctuated with the sound of the whippoorwill. Several times they think they are being followed. Finally they reach their destination and collapse near the river bank. There are clumps of bushes along the bank.

HEDY You go on alone, Tom. I can't. I've got to stop and rest. I bet Moses went on. We've walked for hours.

TOM You can't stop now, Hedy.

HEDY Sh. Down there. Who's that?

They crouch down. Slowly a shape comes towards them. **Moses** *enters. She has a deep scar on her forehead, like a dent, and old scars on the back of her neck. She is thirty-seven years old, five feet tall and has a rich, husky voice. She calls like a whippoorwill.*

TOM *whispers* Are you Moses?

MOSES *nods* What are you children doing down here? Down here by the river bank this time of night. It's dangerous. Your mama and papa gonna be mighty worried.

TOM *rises* We wanna go with you.

MOSES Go? Where, child? Just where do you think I'm plannin' on going?

HEDY Oh, Tom, she's not gonna take us. You said she was the tallest woman in the world and she'd take us North, and you were wrong the whole time.

She starts to cry.

MOSES *bends down. Sees* **Hedy's** *feet are torn and bleeding. Lifts them* You done come a long way, child, to find me.

5

TOM   We been looking for you all night. We ran away from home. You gotta take us.

MOSES   Is that any way to ask a question? Why'd you run away?

Tom looks embarrassed.

HEDY   Tom stole a peach. That's why, and Master Ed beat him!

MOSES   *notices wound, says gently*   You won't get far stealin' Tom.

TOM   *humbly*   I know.

HEDY   And then, Miss Nancy said she was gonna **sell** Tom!

TOM   *pleading*   Moses, please take us with you! We want a chance to grow up free. If I go back to Master Ed now, he'll sell me down river, and I'll never have another chance to get away. We mean to be free, Hedy and me.

MOSES   And once you get free, what do you mean to do?

TOM   I mean to be somebody . . . Not like Master Ed neither. But somebody I'm proud of . . . inside. And Hedy's gonna be a lady. A fine lady. And she's gonna learn to read and write along with me, and . . .

MOSES   *interrupts laughing*   Well, now before you two children turn into the finest lady and the smartest gentleman that this world ever seen, we gotta get North first.   *Looks at the two small figures before her, uncertain that they can make the hard journey*   But this freedom train is goin' a long way. And the road ain't easy. You've got to sleep by day, walk by night. And never let folks know you're about. Watch me. You'll learn to hide as well as I can. You gotta walk so quiet that there's not even a sound of your bare feet on the earth. When you sleep, you gotta be so quiet that there's not a sound of breathing. Not a cough or a sneeze. Once this train starts, ain't no turning back.

TOM   Don't want to go back . . . ever!

HEDY   Ever.

MOSES   You're sure?

TOM   We're sure.

Hedy nods.

6

MOSES *looks up at sky* It's near daylight. We'll wait right here. There'll be two coming to meet me here. *Thoughtfully takes out pistol* And I reckon there'll be a heavy price on the man's head.

TOM Is that why you got a pistol?

MOSES To protect us all, Tom. So no one falls off this train. *Points to North Star* Got to follow that star, and it's a long way off yet.

She crouches in the bushes, so she can barely be seen. **Hedy** *crouches down beside her.*

HEDY How can you tell if you're looking at the right one?

MOSES That's easy. The star up there never moves. It doesn't rise in the East or set in the West as the other stars seem to. Anyone walking towards it could use it as a guide, because it never moves. *To* **Tom** *and* **Hedy** Come on, children. You've got to melt in with the bushes.

TOM Then you will take us?

HEDY Please!

MOSES I never said 'No', yet.

They hug each other, then exit.

Act One
SCENE TWO

A grass swamp area. There is an oak tree with Spanish moss in the centre. There are the noises of the swamp at night and the swish of the river against the bank.
Joe enters, followed by **Linda.** *Joe is in his mid-thirties, handsome, muscular, and a former overseer of a plantation.* **Linda** *is seventeen, delicate, spoiled and a former lady's maid on a large plantation.*

LINDA *sits down* Joe, I'm not walkin' another step. I'm tired. We been walkin' and hidin' for a week now, since we met up with Moses and the two children. If she's so good at gettin' people North, how come there ain't no more along? And how come we ain't there yet? I think the old woman's crazy.

JOE   She ain't crazy, Linda, so none of that foolish talk. Why, a week's nothing. Sometimes it takes months. *Sits beside her*   Nothing's happened to us yet either, Linda, remember that. You and me gotta be careful. Remember we run away. I was hired out to be overseer of a plantation, and you were right there in the big house as a lady's maid. They're gonna be looking for us – soon – if they ain't looking already. There's no turning back just 'cause your feet's sore. It's a miracle we ain't dead, Linda. If it weren't for Moses, we would be. She sure do know where to hide out.

LINDA   *sarcastically*   Strange houses where we hide in secret rooms, or in potato holes in cabins, or sleeping all day in a hollowed out haystack in the fields. I thought I was gonna die from chokin' in that stuff. I've had enough.

JOE   But you didn't die. She knows what she's doing.

LINDA   Joe, it ain't a woman's job to lead us, it don't make no sense.

MOSES   *enters with **Tom** and **Hedy***   Nobody asked whether I was man or woman when they put an axe in my hand and tied me by the waist to a mule. I been doing man's work all my life. I'm not afraid.   *Gives **Tom** and **Hedy** a scarf from her neck*   Here, fill this with all the berries you can find.

***Tom** and **Hedy** work nearby throughout scene.*

LINDA   Joe, I never should have listened to you. It's all your fault with your talk about a better life. Well, if this is the life, I don't like it. I don't see no tables lined with food or people welcomin' us. My dress is nearly torn off from briars pokin' at it, and my feet are covered with blisters and sores. As far as I can see, I ain't no better off than I was two weeks ago when I was still a lady's maid. I don't want to suffer like this for some fool notion in your head about freedom. All I want now is just to eat and sleep regular.

JOE   *angry*   Just some fool notion? Do you think your mistress would welcome you back if you went and said that to her? Do you think she'd throw her arms around you and say, 'Linda, honey, we sure did miss you'?

***Joe** takes out a bowie knife and sharpens it on rock throughout scene.*

MOSES It's too late, Linda. You're a runaway, remember that. You can't go back. You're wanted dead or alive and you're another man's property until you cross that line further north. If you don't want to go with us, then you'll die right here. I won't let you talk to anyone . . . anyone, you hear, about our plans. Too many lives are at stake, and one scared, skinny young miss is not gonna stop my Underground Railroad, and the chance of Joe here and Tom and Hedy to go free!

JOE And your chance too, Linda, if you'd think a minute.

LINDA *subdued, but still complaining* I don't want to think. I'm tired. None of us wanna go further. It ain't worth this travellin', footsore, backs achin', bellies achin'.

TOM *realizing how tired he is* When will we get there, Moses?

HEDY *joining in* I don't reckon I can walk much further.

MOSES Yes, you can!

LINDA *bitter* Besides, what makes you so sure it'll be any better when we get North? At least we were alive in Maryland. Where's this Canada we're heading for? I never heard of it before. This crazy talk about a North Star. There are as many stars in the sky as grains of sand on the earth. It says so in the Bible. So how do you know which one's the North Star for sure? Have you got a special message from up above? We may be heading right back for Maryland.

MOSES *firmly* We're headin' for WILMINGTON, Delaware, and when you get there you'll be fed.

LINDA *sceptical* Fed?

MOSES *the time has come to boost their spirits* Listen to me. There's a man in Wilmington, a Quaker with a wide brimmed hat. He calls himself Thomas Garrett. He don't dress like us or look like us . . . face as pale as cow's milk, but he's our friend and he's gonna give each one of you a pair of shoes to wear North and fresh milk and bread to eat soon as we get there.

HEDY A pair of shoes? Honest? Real shoes?

MOSES New shoes.

TOM *uncertain* Milk? Bread? Do you mean it? Or are you just sayin' it to make us feel better?

MOSES No, it's true. Thomas Garrett keeps a pail of milk and a loaf of bread always ready, always fresh, for God's poor that come to his door.

LINDA God's poor. That sure is us alright.

MOSES He's got a shoe store and one side wall of this shoe store swings open. Behind it is a whole room for us where we can be safe and sleep before goin' on.

LINDA *sarcastically to* **Joe** In our new shoes. Sure. Well, I don't believe it. It sounds like crazy talk. Stories. I want to know where she's really takin' us?

MOSES For the last time, we're goin' to Wilmington. I've made this trip eight times, and we've made it safely. Some folks say it can't be done. But it can be done. It's been done. And it's gonna be done once more. And at the end of the ride you're gonna stand tall – be proud of who you are – be proud of what you done.

LINDA Proud, nothin'. As I see it, it still amounts to the same thing. You can work from sunup to sundown for someone else.

JOE Don't you understand nothin? You can work for yourself. Up there in Canada, I hear folks like us go to school and some do the teaching in the school. Ain't that something? Something to live up to? *Laughs softly* Maybe to tell my grandchildren.

HEDY The way Tom talks about it, it's like there's nothing between you and the sun.

LINDA *to* **Moses** Is that why you do it? Make all these trips?

MOSES We all God's children, ain't we? Every time I go home there's more to come back for. When I was Tom's and Hedy's age, I used to see half starved runaways brought back. I cried when I saw some of them whipped, some sent South with a chain gang to work in the rice fields or in the hot sun of the sugar and cotton plantations. I began to wonder about the other runaways I didn't see come back. Master said he'd sold them or, to frighten us, he'd say that the dogs ate them. But I didn't believe it. So I began to wonder how come none of them didn't come back? How come no one ever said, 'You can do it, too'? That's why I keep goin' back. I tell 'em . . . and I take 'em.

LINDA Well, I ain't no hero like you. I'm goin back. No one treated me bad at the big house. I ate regular anyhow, and I slept at night instead of creepin' through swamps.

MOSES *takes out pistol, points it at* **Linda's** *shoulder blades, calmly* No, Linda, there's no goin' back on this road. Move ahead, or die here.

TOM I don't see what she came for in the first place.

LINDA It was Joe. He came to me talkin' about freedom, and I got to thinkin' about what he said. The folks in the big house treated me alright. But after that, every time I went to eat the food burned with master ownin' it. And I knew Joe was right. I was just another piece of property. And I got to thinkin' how plantation air could never be sweet – no matter how many flowers were bloomin' there.

HEDY If you feel like that, what are you fussin' about?

LINDA I didn't know walkin' to freedom was goin' to be like this. I know I can't walk clear to another country.

JOE *pleading* C'mon Linda. Don't ruin everything. Come with us. Please. I'll help you. Moses will help you. Ain't no better conductor in the whole Underground Railroad. You'll see. We'll make it.

LINDA *turns, slowly, to join them* I'll try.

MOSES *happy at* **Linda's** *decision* Now, no more stops tonight. If you're tired, keep goin'. If you're scared, keep goin'. If you're hungry, keep goin'. If you want to taste freedom, keep goin'.

They begin walking. There is the sound of hoofbeats. The sound is low at first but it increases in volume as the scene progresses.

JOE *in a panic, freezes* They're coming for me, Moses. Hear 'em.

There is the sound of dogs in the distance.

HEDY *frightened* Oh, is Miss Nancy comin' after us?

LINDA *starts to cry* I told you. I told you. Oh? We're all gonna die.

11

MOSES Sh. All of you. Break off some pine branches.

TOM What for?

MOSES *ignores him* Linda, tear up your petticoat. We're gonna fool those dogs . . .

*Tom brings over pine branches and **Linda** and **Hedy** give her strips of petticoat. **Moses** works as she talks. She distributes pine boughs and rags to each.*

Take this pine bough and take this rag and tie a tail on yourself that will brush behind you the whole way. That's all the hounds is ever gonna smell is plain old pine trees. This freedom train is just startin'. It ain't got up its high speed. And fears gotta ride on this train. Right up front with us. Make friends with it. Shake its hand. It's one of the angels that's ridin' with us, protectin' you, remindin' you to be steady, silent and careful. It's gonna get a lot colder as we get on – and you're all gonna go hungry. But at the end of the ride, God willin', we're gonna be free. We're gonna be free and safe and happy.

*They tie them on. **Hedy** starts to laugh at **Tom**.*

HEDY You look funny, Tom.

MOSES Hush, child. Not a sound. Take your brother's hand, Hedy. Joe, take Linda's hand.

*Moses takes **Hedy's** hand.*

We're gonna make a chain for the next few miles. When I stop, you stop. If I fall to the ground, you fall to the ground. Don't breathe a word.

The children start as if it's a game.

Now listen. Any old body can go through the woods crashing and mashing things down like a cow. That's easy. You gotta move like an Injun. So quiet, even a bird in the nest don't hear you – and fly up. So quiet, not even a leaf makes a rustle. Not even a twig cracks back on itself when you come through them. *Points to the star, and they begin* Remember that's where this train is goin'.

*This section can be choreographed. As they walk, **Moses** stops dead. They all freeze. She listens. They continue. Behind it all, there is the steady rhythm of horses' hoofbeats and the sound of hounds in pursuit. At one point **Moses*** *drops to the ground, and they drop too. The tension and weariness mount. Suddenly, **Moses** points to the sky and in the distance a rooster is heard announcing dawn. There is now silence around them, and they realize they are safe for the moment. The sky is visibly lighter.*

We've lost them. We're safe for a while. Joe, see if you can get us a swamp rabbit. The rest of you sleep while you can.

*Silently they find spots to hide and sleep amongst the bushes and undergrowth. **Moses** kneels and prays. **Hedy** crawls to her and tugs at her sleeve. **Moses** goes on praying. **Hedy** tugs again.*

HEDY *whining* I'm hungry.

MOSES Go to sleep.

She goes on praying.

HEDY *doesn't budge* I'm hungry. Ain't had nothin' to eat since yesterday.

MOSES *firmly* When you wake up, we'll eat.

HEDY But I'm hungry now.

MOSES Well, I reckon we could all do with a good meal, Hedy; but there isn't enough food for that. Maybe later tonight Joe will catch us a swamp rabbit.

HEDY I could eat a whole one myself. Right now. Without cooking it first, even. Moses, when we go underground, will there be food then?

MOSES *laughing gently* What are you talking about, Hedy?

HEDY Tom said you led people underground and when they got there, everything was fine and beautiful – and when they came up, they were free, just like that.

She starts to cry from exhaustion, hunger and fear.

MOSES *holds her in her arms* Oh, honey, it ain't gonna be like that. It's gonna be on this real earth and we're gonna be creepin' North in the night through trees and swamps, because we've got plenty of enemies around us by daylight.

HEDY *fresh outburst of sobs* I wanna go home. I wanna go home. I miss Mama and Papa.

MOSES *comforting her* Sure you do, honey. And I'll bet they're thinking of you too. Right now. Hedy, can you see that star up there? *Hedy looks up and nods* It's almost mornin'! You can barely see it now. But it's travelled millions of miles so you could see its light every night. And it's tellin' you to be brave, not to give up now. Millions of miles just to tell you that.

HEDY *slowly, questioningly* I guess if that star can go all that way, I guess I can go a little further, maybe. Only when we gonna get there, Moses, when?

MOSES Why, honey, we only been walking a little more than a week. I reckon we'll be in Wilmington soon. But then we gotta go clear to Canada.

HEDY Why we gotta go all that way? Why can't we just stay with the man who's gonna give us all new shoes? Can I pick any colour I want?

MOSES Them shoes is to help you walk and the colour does not matter. Anymore of that lazy girl talk, and you won't get any shoes at all, Miss Hedy.

HEDY *subdued* Is Canada very far? Very cold?

MOSES Yes, it is.

HEDY Why do we have to go so far?

MOSES Didn't used to, Hedy. But seven years ago in 1850 . . .

HEDY What happened then?

MOSES Now child, if you'd stop askin' so many questions and give me a chance to answer, I'd tell you. Seven years ago the government passed a law. Said runaway slaves couldn't have a trial by jury. Said they'd punish anyone tryin' to help us escape.

HEDY Punish?

MOSES If some people find out Mr Garrett is helpin' us, they may just put him in jail.

HEDY Why?

MOSES Because the law says they can. Sometimes folks who are scared act like cowards and sometimes they pass laws to make them sound brave. They call the law the New Fugitive Slave law. Sounds important. But inside you know the men who passed it were just scared.

HEDY Scared of what? Of me? What for? I wouldn't hurt no one. Neither would Tom. You just ask him.

MOSES Scared that you and Tom and others like you really mean to be free . . . to stand tall. *Crisply* So, since I can't trust Uncle Sam with our people no longer, I gotta take 'em even further . . . up to Canada. And when we get there, you gotta promise me you're gonna learn to read, Hedy, and write and you're gonna amount to somethin' and folks are gonna say, 'There goes Hedy. She's some fine brave girl'.

HEDY I'm gonna try, Moses. I'm really gonna try. But I don't think I'll ever be as brave as you.

MOSES Hush, now, honey. You sleep awhile. You gotta rest to grow up taller.

She puts her shawl around her and sings softly a chorus of 'Go down, Moses'.

Lights come up softly and then fade to indicate the day has passed and it is now twilight. **Moses** *is asleep with* **Hedy** *in her arms.* **Linda** *and* **Tom** *are asleep, nearby.* **Joe** *enters, shakes* **Moses** *urgently.*

JOE *whispers* I went near the road. There wasn't anyone around. But it looked like a horse team had gone by — maybe a few hours ago. Looks like they lost this on the way.

MOSES *picks up poster* A runaway poster. About you Joe? *He nods* Read it to me.

JOE *scans it* 'Reward, $1,000. Wanted alive. Valuable man.' Valuable man! First time I ever heard that.

MOSES Does it go on to give your name and a description of you?

JOE *nods, reads to himself, then aloud* 'Believed to be heading North.'

TOM *incredulous* Joe! Can you read?

JOE Enough to know we're in trouble.

TOM *nudging* **Hedy** Hedy, Joe can really read!

MOSES *jumps to her feet, wakes* **Linda** Come on children. We're gonna have to leave this place . . . now . . . fast. We're still in danger. We're gonna wade in the water so no one will see our footprints. We gotta go a long way tonight, and even your breathin's gotta be soft. We're in trouble. Someone's lookin' for us and lookin' right around here, and if they find us, we'll never live to tell about it.

Lights dim to show passage of time. Lights up. They are making their way precariously along the river bank.

TOM *whispers* Moses, I'm cold.

MOSES Sh.

Clap of thunder. **Hedy** *starts to scream and* **Tom** *covers her mouth. Lightning flashes in the sky.*

LINDA Storm comin'. We better stop and find shelter.

MOSES No shelter tonight. We gotta keep movin'. If the heavens all open up, we gotta keep goin'. Only a few more miles and then we can stop. We've got to cross that line into Delaware or nothin' will matter again.

TOM Moses, it's beginning to rain!

MOSES I know, honey. Praise God there's no moon and there's a fog rollin' in. Ain't no one gonna see us tonight. You've been out before in the rain, Hedy. Didn't hurt you before. Won't hurt you now. You just follow me.

HEDY How do you know we're even goin' in the right direction? We can't see the North Star now.

MOSES Come here, and I'll show you. You feel the bark on the tree, this way. There, can you feel the side the moss is thickest on?

HEDY *feels tree* **Yes!**

TOM What good does that do?

MOSES The north side of the tree hardly ever gets sun. That means it's the north side where the moss grows thickest.

TOM It's cold. I ain't never been so cold before, Moses.

MOSES *lifts her head up, taking in the air. It is sharp and biting. She is jubilant* There's a north wind, Tom. Come clear from Canada. There'll be frost on the ground tonight. Praise God! We're getting there! *Stops* We cross the river there. It's the narrowest part.

She steps into the river – on the side of the stage, so they will exit into the wings.

16

LINDA   You gonna wade that river?

MOSES   Runnin' water leaves no trace. And we gotta cross it here. We gotta cross that line.

LINDA   That does it. I'll wade no freezin' water for no crazy woman.

*Joe follows **Moses.***

JOE   I'm coming Moses.

LINDA   Joe, don't leave us.

TOM   Look, it's up to her knees.

LINDA   It's up to his waist.

HEDY   It's up to her chin.   *Pause. They watch, fearing the worst.*

TOM, HEDY, LINDA   They made it!

LINDA   Joe's waving to us. C'mon children. He's coming back to help us cross.

HEDY   I'm scared, Linda. The water's high.

LINDA   *stronger*   Now, remember what Moses said: 'If you're scared, keep going!'.

*She takes **Tom's** and **Hedy's** hands and prepares to cross the river.*

Act Two
SCENE ONE

*The interior of **Thomas Garrett's** Quaker home in Wilmington, Delaware. There is the front room, a shoe store with a front door up centre. To the right is an old wooden desk and chair. Stage right on the diagonal is a wall lined with shoe boxes. A few boots and shoes are displayed. In front of the wall are chairs for customers. One panel of this wall leads to the secret room, stage left. The room is dark and windowless. On the floor are a few pallets and blankets to lie on. At the back of this room there is a water pitcher, basin, and a thick candle on a stand. It is just before dawn. There are three knocks in rapid succession. These are repeated a second time.*

THOMAS *enters, wearing traditional Quaker garb, appropriate for the late hour. He opens the door slightly* Who goes there?

MOSES Friend. *She uses the secret code* I have four parcels with me.

THOMAS *opens the door wide* Come in quickly, friends. I have room and thee are welcome. *Hedy is half asleep. Thomas carries her in. Joe carries Linda, who is ill. Moses and Tom enter* Sit down, my friends. Sit down. *Carries over a pail of milk, ladle, and tin cups* I am glad to see thee, Moses. I was not sure if thee was alive or dead.

He serves the milk.

MOSES Alive, praise the Lord! But I have a risky cargo. Joe here has $1,000 on his head.

THOMAS *takes a loaf of bread from desk and slices it* Joe . . . yes . . . I think I saw the poster. We shall do our best to make sure no one gets that reward while you are here.

Distributes bread Is the girl ill?

JOE Linda's been bad since yesterday.

THOMAS Let us hope that rest will help, for I dare not call a doctor.

HEDY *wakes up sleepily* Moses, I'm hungry.

THOMAS *with affection* I see thee are hungry, child, and tired. Thee must have food and rest.

HEDY *to Tom* Why does he talk so funny?

TOM Sh! Moses said he was a Quaker, and they all talk that way. *Munching the bread* Everything's just like Moses said.

THOMAS I see thee will need new shoes.

HEDY It was all true. It really was!

THOMAS *to Moses* Can thee rest here today? This evening I will send you on. There is more danger at present than before.

LINDA More danger, Lord, I can't go on. I can't.

MOSES She has been ill since yesterday, but we had to get to your house before we could risk stopping.

18

Thomas puts his hands on her forehead to see if she has a temperature.

LINDA   *shakes him away*   No! No! Go away.

THOMAS   *gently*   Thee needs rest and care. I will do what I can. Sit down for a moment, friend.

LINDA   So tired. So tired.

She dozes off.

HEDY   Thank you for the bread, Mr Garrett.

TOM   And the milk.

HEDY   *impatiently*   And will we really get shoes? New shoes?

MOSES   *laughing*   Hedy! Thomas Garrett, there are two North Stars, one in heaven, and one right here. We would be lost without your help.

THOMAS   Thee knows, I hope by now, that your knock will never go unanswered as long as I live in this house.

MOSES   *gratefully*   Children, this is our greatest friend in the North.

THOMAS   *shakes his head*   No.   *Humbly*   It is He that inspires us to do the work He requires of our hands, and it is He that is your greatest friend. Moses, I am glad to see thee in good health and ready for action.   *Softly to her so children won't hear*   The highway is not safe. Some slaves escaped nearby and there is great excitement. None of us are safe. They suspect I helped.   *To **Tom** and **Hedy***   Thee had better hide now and sleep out of sight.

TOM   Where? I don't see a place to hide.

Thomas pushes wall panel and panel springs open.

TOM   Look at that!

HEDY   A secret room!

THOMAS   Here thee will be safe. Rest now. Thee has a long journey ahead. I will call thee when it is time to leave, when it is safe.

*He carries in remainder of food and milk. **Joe** assists **Linda**, puts her on pallet. **Moses, Tom** and **Hedy** walk in.*

LINDA   *half asleep*   Where am I? It looks like jail.

She begins to cry.

THOMAS I will light the candle, so thee will not be fearful. *Lights candle* But thee must be silent. One sneeze, one cry, one cough, and thee will be found if there are unexpected visitors. Rest, my friends, and finish thy food, but in silence.

Exits, closes panel. **Tom** *and* **Hedy** *lie down.* **Moses** *adjusts the blankets over them and* **Joe** *puts a blanket over* **Linda.** **Thomas** *sits at his desk in the front room, lights a lamp, takes a quill pen and dips it into the ink pot. He writes the following note:*

'To William Still: Philadelphia. Respected friend, this evening I send to thee four of God's poor. May success attend them in their efforts to maintain themselves. Please send words whether or not these seven arrived safe I wrote thee of ten days ago. My wife and self are as ever thy friends, Thomas Garrett.'

As he puts his pen down, there is a loud, sharp knock at the door. **Garrett** *looks surprised, snuffs out candle and hides letter. He opens the door slightly.*

Who goes there?

Two men force their way in, one flourishing a pistol and the other a bowie knife. They look around briefly.

FIRST MAN Where are they?

SECOND MAN Where are they hiding?

In the secret room **Tom** *wakes up. He listens terrified by the wall.* **Moses** *and* **Hedy** *wake up.* **Hedy** *starts to ask a question.* **Moses** *covers* **Hedy's** *mouth gently, hugs her, adjusts her blanket.* **Moses** *and* **Tom** *listen intently while others sleep.*

THOMAS Friend, thee has wakened me. Pray lower thy voice.

FIRST MAN We'll wake up the whole household if we have to. Come on. Out with it. Where are they?

THOMAS If you mean my wife, she is upstairs and I pray not wakened by your loud noise. I am, as thee can see, awake and in front of you, though thee knows God meant for good men to sleep until the sun rose.

FIRST MAN   We know you've got slaves here, Garrett. So you can cut out the holy talk   *Flourishes knife*   Seems to me you lost all your property once before for helping slaves and giving them breakfast! Heard you lost all you owned. Did they thank you for it, Thomas Garrett? Did they?   *Knife is near his throat*   If you cooperate with us, Garrett, you'll live a lot longer.

THOMAS   *calmly pushes aside weapon. With disdain*   No one but a coward resorts to such means to carry out his ends.

SECOND MAN   We're after slaves, Tom Garrett. Not sermons.

THOMAS   In my home, and despite what you may hear, it is still my home, it is the word of God thee will hear, and none other. If thee does not like its peaceful sound, thee is free to leave!

FIRST MAN   *changing his tactics*   Garrett, we know they're in here somewhere. Even if you can hide them for three weeks, when they sneak out, we'll get them. There's $1,000 on the man . . . he won't get away. Not with that price on his head!

THOMAS   *tries to hide his concern*   Thee has strange information. How comes thee by it?

SECOND MAN   So they are here! By poster, Garrett, all over the country. A good description, too. You can't get away with it any longer. The law will catch up with you.

THOMAS   My law is God's law. If thee does not respect it, thee is not welcome in my home nor has thee a right to be here.

SECOND MAN   We'll catch you helping them soon enough, Garrett. We'll get you and put you out in the street with no place to go. See if your God protects you then. We're just waiting . . . and remember, the new law is on our side.

THOMAS   It's the Devil's law!

FIRST MAN   Call it what you will . . . 'Devil's law' or 'New Fugitive Slave law', it was passed seven years ago and it hasn't been changed.

SECOND MAN   Let us refresh Mr Garrett's memory. A man can lose all his property for giving food, shelter and assistance to slaves. Or have you forgotten so quickly?

THOMAS There are no slaves in my house. In the past, God's poor have passed through, but in His eyes we are all equal. *Reflects* However, I am not sure what His opinion of thee would be.

FIRST MAN I'm warning you, if you've got fugitive slaves in this house, now, they won't get past the Delaware border. There are police at both ends of the bridge and even at other crossing points.

THOMAS Thank you for the warning, gentlemen. *Firmly, ushering them out* I have only a few dollars left in the world, but if thee know a fugitive who needs breakfast, send him to me.

SECOND MAN Garrett, you'll go to prison.

THOMAS If this be a crime for which one goes to prison, then there must be some excellent people there. Now if thee will excuse me, I have work to do. The sun is up. An appropriate moment for a night call to end, I think.

Opens door and firmly ushers them out. He stands there against the door for a moment to recover from the ordeal. His wife appears.

SARAH Again, Thomas?

THOMAS Again.

SARAH Will they not let us sleep?

THOMAS They know.

SARAH Who is here?

THOMAS Moses and four others. They want the reward money.

SARAH *angrily* They belong to the Devil.

THOMAS And they will return to him, my dear, never fear.

SARAH Oh, Thomas, it isn't fair. Some say women are weaker than men, but look at Moses. She's gone back eight times . . . alone, despite the danger, to free more slaves . . . a handful at a time. That's all she can take. And so she will go, again and again, until she dies or until the world comes to its senses. Is it right that such a woman should have to crawl along, tree by tree, and pray to pass unnoticed, while other men are free by law to hunt her down and be honoured for the deed?

THOMAS   My dear, be glad she goes unnoticed and yet I wish it were more unnoticed. And as for honour, that will come, someday. God chooses strong people to do His work, but He never promised any that it would be easy. Did the men wake thee?

SARAH   The noise did. Thomas, he had a gun. I saw it. It seemed to be the very shape of a devil.

THOMAS   *firm, calmly*   Yes, he had a gun. But we have reason and human kindness on our side.

SARAH   Oh, Thomas, is that any good against a knife and a gun?

THOMAS   Yes.   *Pause*   Provided we know how to use them.

SARAH   How long will Moses stay?

THOMAS   I'll send them on tonight, but not by the way I planned. That way is too dangerous, now. There will be police at the entrance of the bridge. That much information I just received from the Devil's own aides.

SARAH   How, then?

THOMAS   *sits thinking*   A friend drives the bricklayers across the bridge to work . . . Yes, yes! That's a common enough sight. The men go over singing and shouting. No one stops them. And at nightfall they return. Still singing and shouting. Moses only brought four. Yes, they can lie on the bottom of the wagon and under the boards. Yes. Yes. We could do it.
Jovial   Make a large breakfast, Mrs Garrett. I'm hungry enough for six people this morning.

SARAH   *laughing*   Thomas Garrett, I'm glad I married thee.

THOMAS   Why?

SARAH   My mother always said a man with such a big appetite must have as big a heart as well. Eggs for them, Thomas!

THOMAS   Yes. Eggs, milk, bread. Two are children, Sarah. They are very thin . . . frightened.

SARAH   And eggs and milk for thee, Thomas. Thee looks thin, too.

THOMAS   Nonsense, with all those big breakfasts thee makes!

SARAH   They go to others, I know. Now, promise me, Thomas. Thee needs nourishment too, to go on with thy work.

Exits.

THOMAS   If they escape this time, it will be God's miracle. If no one sees them, and if they don't suffocate . . . but it's the only way . . . the only chance . . . we've got to try it!

Act Two
SCENE TWO

*The outskirts of Wilmington. There is a bridge going from up centre to down left. Down right there is a large bush. Several townspeople cross the bridge. **Sarah** crosses with a market basket. The two men are standing at the edge of the bridge watching each passerby. **First Man** smokes a cigar. **Second Man** doffs his hat when he sees **Sarah**. A **Policeman** stands on duty, watchful.*

SECOND MAN   Good morning, Ma'am. Fine day. Clear as can be. Can see for miles.

FIRST MAN   I was just saying it was nice weather to stand here and have a smoke.

SARAH   *coldly*   It's a fine day for work, gentlemen. I wonder that thee hast none to keep thee busy.

Exits quickly.

FIRST MAN   *nudges the other*   No work, she says! By midnight you and I will be $1,500 richer.

SECOND MAN $1,500?

FIRST MAN   *sorry he mentioned it*   Didn't you know? Reward's gone up. Five hundred dollars more.

SECOND MAN   How do you know we'll catch them by tonight? Maybe they got away already. We haven't seen anything.

FIRST MAN   Well now, you don't expect them to walk up and say, 'Here I am. Go get your reward'. The trouble with you is you're lazy. You better do your share of the work or you'll lose your share of the money.

SECOND MAN   You're the one who's standing here smoking a big, fancy cigar. Don't try to threaten me.

FIRST MAN   Take it easy. Maybe you should just look under the bridge. Maybe they're creeping along the river bank.

SECOND MAN   Why me? Why don't you go? Afraid to get mud on your shoes?

FIRST MAN   I got to stand here and watch the road.

SECOND MAN   Oh, alright. Anything coming?

There are sounds of singing and shouting in distance.

FIRST MAN   Just the bricklayer's wagon coming up. Same as usual. They sure do make a racket. Go on, hurry up.

Second Man goes. A wagon makes its way across the bridge slowly. Two men are singing, walking beside it. They are stopped by the Policeman. He checks the wagon wheels.

POLICEMAN   Halt! Cargo?

BRICKLAYER   Bricks. Same as usual.

POLICEMAN   Oh, it's you two. Go ahead. No need to check your wagon.

Second Man reappears, reports to First Man.

SECOND MAN   Nothing.

FIRST MAN   Let's go and check the other side of town. He's stopping all the traffic anyway, so they can't escape over this end of the bridge.

They exit. Wagon turns off bridge and goes to bush. Bricklayer walks to back of wagon, knocks three times. Slowly, painfully, Moses, Hedy, Tom, Linda and Joe creep out. All are wearing new shoes.

BRICKLAYER   Run for it. I don't dare stop long. Good luck.

They thank him

BRICKLAYER   Run!

HEDY   C'mon, beautiful new shoes. We're going North.

MOSES   This way! Not a sound.

TOM   Ain't we free yet, Moses? I'm tired.

MOSES   Mean to be free, Tom. But we ain't free yet. Now, down on your bellies and crawl!

They do so. The wagon moves on.

Act Two
SCENE THREE

Oliver Johnson's Anti-Slavery Office, New York City, 1857. On the wall there is a large 'Wanted' poster which reads $1,500. In the upper left-hand corner is a black woodcut of a small running figure with a stick over his shoulder, a bundle tied to the end of a stick and another stick in his hand. This is the symbol of the runaway slave. The legend reads: 'Joe Bailey ran away from his subscriber on Saturday night, October 12, 1857. He is about 5'10" in height, chestnut colour, bald head with a remarkable skin. $1,500 to anyone who will apprehend said Joe Bailey and lodge him safely in jail at Aston Talbot County, Maryland.' **Oliver Johnson** *is at his desk.* **Moses, Hedy, Tom, Linda** *and* **Joe** *enter.* **Moses** *is dressed in a man's suit. There are briars clinging to it. It is old, worn and snagged. She wears a felt hat and men's shoes on her feet.*

OLIVER JOHNSON   Harriet Tubman! We just had word from William Still in Philadelphia that you were on your way.   *Glances at poster on wall and studies Joe*   And this is Joe Bailey, if I'm not mistaken. I am glad to see the man who is worth $1,500 to his master.

JOE   *trembling*   Mr Johnson, how did you know me?

OLIVER   *points to poster*   The poster's right here in our office and the description's so close that no one could mistake it. Welcome. Sit down, all of you. How did you get here?

HEDY   We rode at the bottom of a bricklayer's wagon out of Wilmington.

OLIVER   *laughs*   Well, they'd never think to look there for you.

MOSES   Children, this is Oliver Johnson, head of the New York Anti-Slavery Office. And this is Hedy and Tom.

26

They shake hands.

And Linda.

They shake hands.

OLIVER I'm glad to see two such brave children. I'm glad to see all of you . . . here, and safe.

JOE But Mr Johnson, what am I going to do now? If you recognized me, and you never saw me before, how am I ever going to make it? $1,500!

TOM *admiring poster, tracing figure with his finger* What'd you do, Joe? How come they're willing to pay so much for you? Nobody seems even to miss me.

MOSES *hugs **Tom*** You just thank the good Lord they ain't out lookin' for you, child.

JOE Mr Martin hired me out every day. I was an overseer of a plantation. And then I was sold to the same man I'd been working for. $1,000 down and $1,000 to come. My first lesson after I was sold was a beating. Even though I'd worked from early morning to late at night, sun and rain. It didn't matter to him. My first lesson with my new master was a beating. And I went to Moses's Uncle Ben and just said, 'Next time Moses comes, let me know'. *Suddenly angry, ripping poster from wall and crumpling it* Well, they can't stop me now. They can't! I'm going to farm that Canadian land, just the way I planned. And I'm going to build us a home there, just the way I planned. And I'm going to help anyone of us coming North, because that's the way I dreamed it. And that's the way I planned it. Mr Johnson, how far off is Canada now?

OLIVER Three hundred miles to Niagara Falls on the train. When you cross the rise in the tracks, you'll be on the other side, and you'll be free.

JOE *nervous* We're going on the train? An open train? Shouldn't we keep right on going North the same way we got here?

OLIVER Not in the winter. You'd freeze in the cold inside of a week. Besides, the train's so obvious, they won't even think of looking for you there. It's the road, ditches and fields they'll be watching. And it's three hundred more miles, remember.

HEDY   All that way to go, just to be free?

TOM   *to **Hedy***   Moses told us before, it's a long walk to freedom.

OLIVER   And Moses has walked it nearly nine times. Do you still remember the first time, Moses?

MOSES   That's the time I remember most.

TOM   Why?

MOSES   Well, I crossed the line into the free state of Pennsylvania just as the sun was coming up. I looked at my hands to see if I was the same person, now I was free. There was such a glory over everything. The sun came like gold through the trees and over the fields, and I felt like I was in heaven. *Group sits transfixed. **Moses** laughs gently*   But there was no one to welcome me to the land of freedom. I was a stranger in a strange land. And I sat down and thought, 'My home is, after all, way down in the old cabin quarter right there with the old folks and my brothers and sisters'. I was free, and they should be free too. I decided to try and make a home for them up here in the North and, the Lord helping me, I would bring them all here. Oh, how I prayed then, lying all alone on the cold damp ground. I didn't have no friend then, and I needed help.

OLIVER   Harriet, Harriet, you've got to be careful now. There's a $40,000 reward out for your capture. I don't know how you've done it so far.

MOSES   I tell the Lord what I need, and He provides. *Looks around at her group*   We've made it this far. Canada's just further north.

OLIVER   *hands them tickets*   Here are your train tickets. And here are five bibles. There's a bible meeting up North in St Catharines. That's past the border, and you're going to it – if anyone asks.

He hands them the bibles.

HEDY   But I can't read!

OLIVER   Here's your first lesson.
Demonstrates   These white pages always belong on the right side when the gold letters are on the top. The gold letters spell bible. B-I-B-L-E.

HEDY   Tom . . . I'm learning to read, just like you said!

She traces the letters with her fingers.

OLIVER   *distributes winter garments*   Watch out for
the conductor. If he accepts your tickets, he's one of us
and he'll let you cross the border. If he doesn't, be
prepared to jump off that train. And don't talk to the
passengers. They may sound friendly to fool you, but
they may just want to get a better look at you before
they try to collect the reward money. Keep your heads in
these bibles. And you better leave now. Moses, you know
the way to the station.

They all start out except **Linda** *who sits there.*

LINDA   Moses, I want to be free just like Joe said, you
know I do. But I'm tired. I just don't think I can keep on
going three hundred more miles. I don't want to go to no
Canada.

MOSES   Mean to be free. Remember? If I can't trust
Uncle Sam with my people no longer, I can bring 'em up
clear to Canada, and that's what I plan to do. There's two
things you got a right to: liberty or death. If you can't
have one, you can have the other. But no one, hear me,
no one is gonna take any one of us alive, ever. I never run
my train off the track and I never lost a single
passenger. We can fight for our liberty as long as our
strength lasts, and when the time comes for me to go or
for you to go, the Lord will take us in. No one else! I don't
want to hear no more talk of givin' up. Three hundred
miles! Why, that's nothing! Think how many miles we
come so far!

Act Two
SCENE FOUR

*Stage right, a railroad car. Stage left, the platform between
cars. The train is bound for Niagara Falls, Canada.*
Moses, Tom, Hedy, Joe *and* **Linda** *are seated,
pretending to study their bibles.*

CONDUCTOR   *offstage*   Next stop, Niagara Falls,
Ontario. Tickets, all tickets, please.

HEDY   *to* **Tom**   Does that mean Canada? Are we
nearly there?

TOM   Shhhh. Yes. Make believe you're asleep, so he can't ask nothin'. And hold your book up, so he'll think we're free and go to school. Remember what Mr Johnson told you. *Tom studies bible cover, whispers*   Hedy, which way does it go?

HEDY   *looks at it carefully, turns it right side up*   This way . . . I think.

*The **Conductor** enters car. **Tom** nudges **Hedy**.*

TOM   Shhhh.

CONDUCTOR   You young folks have tickets?

*Hedy nods and gives him tickets. **Conductor** examines tickets and looks at them carefully. He looks at **Moses, Joe** and **Linda**.*

You all together?

*They look at one another apprehensively. There is a pause. Slowly, **Moses** answers.*

MOSES   We're together.

CONDUCTOR   *looks at them all closely again. Heartily*   Well now, if you'll just give me your tickets, I won't bother you any longer, and you can go right on with your bible study group. Guess you're all heading up for that meeting in St Catharines, up in Canada?

*Moses nods gratefully. **Conductor** bends down, puts **Hedy's** bible right side up. He goes on down the aisle.*

I'll let you know when we get to the Falls.

*He goes towards platform as the two men come on the platform with the poster announcing reward for **Joe**. They study it carefully.*

FIRST MAN   We've searched nearly every car on this train. Haven't seen him yet.

SECOND MAN   But the man said he saw him get on.

FIRST MAN   You mean we paid a man fifty dollars to tell us that. You can't trust anyone these days. The whole country wants the reward money. Wait till I get my hands on him.

SECOND MAN   C'mon. Let's try the next car. We haven't got much time.

CONDUCTOR *appearing, as men try to conceal poster. They exchange long look* Tickets, gentlemen.

FIRST MAN You have the tickets.

SECOND MAN No, I don't! You do.

He hunts through his own pockets to double-check.

FIRST MAN *bullying him* All right, where'd you put 'em? You better remember . . . quick!

SECOND MAN *scared, remembers* Coat pocket. That's where I put them. Five cars back. Conductor, you'll have to collect them later from us. We're in a hurry.

CONDUCTOR Well, you'll just have to go five cars back and get them.

FIRST MAN Conductor, we're looking for friends. We're supposed to meet them on the train. If you could just let us go into the next car to see if they're there . . .

CONDUCTOR Sorry, gentlemen.

SECOND MAN They'll be worried about us.

CONDUCTOR As far as I know, you gentlemen are riding free on an international railroad. You can't go wandering around a train without your tickets. How am I supposed to do my job?

FIRST MAN But conductor . . .

CONDUCTOR Every passenger must show his ticket upon request as proof he has purchased one. That's the regulation.

FIRST MAN *disgusted* I told you to take those tickets!

SECOND MAN Hurry up. We've still got time.

They exit.

JOE How much longer, Moses?

MOSES Should be soon.

CONDUCTOR Next stop, Niagara. Niagara Falls, Ontario. *Walks to **Tom** and **Hedy*** If you keep watching out that window, you'll see the Falls.

TOM When do we get to Canada?

CONDUCTOR Soon as we hit that rise in the bridge.

He exits, goes to platform.

HEDY   Tom! It's beginning now. Feel it?

LINDA   I can see the Falls!

JOE   Moses, are we here?

MOSES   Almost.

The men reappear attempting to show their tickets to the **Conductor.** *At that moment, everyone is jolted by the centre rise of the track.*

That's it! That bump! That's the centre. You're in Queen
   Victoria's free land. Look at the Falls!

FIRST MAN   *shakes* **Second Man**   Canada! Now,
   what good are those tickets? All this way for nothing!

CONDUCTOR   *quietly*   Nice day to see the Falls,
   gentlemen. As long as you've come this far.

They exit.

LINDA   Oh, Moses, I didn't believe it. I didn't think we'd
   make it.

JOE   On an open train.

LINDA   Oh Joe, after walking all that way . . . we're
   here . . . we're free! Ain't nothing can make you a slave
   again.

*They begin to put on wraps, standing up and gathering
bundles.*

TOM   Now we'll learn to read and write – just like Joe
   can. And no more stealin', I promise.

HEDY   Moses, when we get off the train you're staying
   here with us, aren't you?

JOE   Of course she will. We're all going to stay together
   and . . .

MOSES   *interrupts*   No. Soon as you're settled I'm goin'
   back.

JOE   You can't. There's $40,000 reward out for you.

MOSES   Ain't nobody collected it yet.

LINDA   But it's dangerous.

MOSES   I know.

TOM   Do you have to go?

MOSES   Yes.

LINDA   Oh, Moses, you've done enough already. You've made the trip nine times crawlin' on your belly, goin' hungry. And now all that again? Is it worth it . . . to risk your life?

MOSES   *calmly*   So long as God wants to use me, He'll take care of me.

HEDY   Oh, Tom, I understand now. All this talk about freedom. It means I don't have to crawl on my belly no more, be silent no more, go hungry, no more creepin' in the dark. Every time Moses goes, some more of us stand straight. I can walk right off this train standin' tall as a pine tree, singin' as loud as I can. Singin'. The whole world's gonna hear us.

LINDA   Joe, we're safe. The freedom ride's over.

JOE   *slowly, thoughtfully*   The way I look at it, it's just beginnin'.

33

STAGING THE PLAY

Look carefully at your performance space before you decide how to stage your play. Consider how you can use its features to the best advantage. If there is a proscenium stage or a platform with curtains, you might be able to extend the acting area by placing platforms or rostra in front of the stage. Is there room to perform your play with the audience on three sides of the action? Can you use different levels to suggest different scenes? How will the actors get in and out of the acting space efficiently? If your play can be performed in the round, you may be able to use routes through the audience to suggest the progression of the journey.

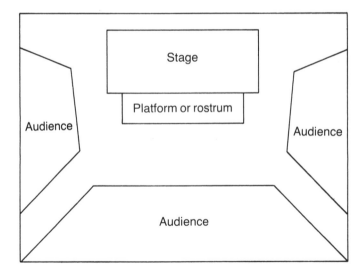

Because the play takes place in a number of different locations, the set for your performance will need to be as flexible as possible. Keep props and scenery to a minimum. If time is spent on laborious scene changes, the excitement of the story will be lost. Try to suggest specific locations by the use of simple props and furniture – a washing bucket and clothes for the first scene, for example. The 'Wanted' poster for Harriet Tubman might be used as a prop.

Effective lighting will be important. If each area can be lit separately, the change from scene to scene will be smoother. At the end of each scene, the lighting will fade on the area of action, the actors will move to their next position and the lights will come up on them once they are in place. You may be able to use special effects – for example, moonlight – when the runaways are on the road.

Characters

Much of the effect of the play will depend on the characters being convincing, particularly the runaways and 'Moses'. You will need to convey the courage and determination that was required of all the people involved in the Underground Railroad. Depending on the actors available, you can change the number of characters who appear in the play. The number of runaways can be increased and the men's and women's parts can be altered, although Harriet needs to be female.

Experiment with the play in rehearsal, and improvise some extra scenes, or add some of the ideas for dramatic activities suggested in the resource material. Try to regard the play as a framework for your own explorations about characters' past lives. If you are playing a character like Linda, who is selfish and frightened, try to build up another side of her character. What kind of courage might she find? Ask yourself questions about your character, so that you are not just presenting a stereotype, but a more fully developed character.

Costumes

Costumes should be kept very simple – worn, ragged jeans, long cotton skirts and torn shirts will be suitable for the runaways. Other characters, like the Quakers, should be simply dressed with a suggestion of 19th century clothing: long dark dresses, shawls and aprons for the women, and dark suits with high collars for the men.

Music

Music could be an important element in staging the play. You might choose to have a small singing group or choir at one side of the acting area. This group could sing a number of different spirituals or folk songs between scenes, or over action sequences. Unaccompanied voices would work very well, or you could choose to have a guitarist, a pianist or a small instrumental group. If you use music in this way, keep it simple, so that the power of the authentic songs can come across. There are songs and spirituals on pages 66–68, but you might also include hymns like 'Amazing Grace', or more modern songs associated with the civil rights movement like 'We Shall Overcome'.

Slide projections

An effective and simple way of providing 'scenery' would be to use slide or back projections. You will need a large screen at the back of your acting area and one, or preferably two, carousel projectors. You could project slides of the plantation, the mansion, the night sky, various locations on the journey, maps showing the escape route, 'Wanted' posters for the runaways – or just use the screen to give atmosphere to each location. Slides can be prepared from photographs or created specially for the show.

Choral speaking

At the beginning of the play, on page xiii, is the last verse of the poem *Runagate, Runagate*. It is about the events of the play – an exciting piece, and full of atmosphere. It is particularly suitable for choral speaking. A group of voices presenting the verse in this way will provide an arresting introduction to your play.

ACTIVITIES ON AND AROUND THE PLAY

1 Reasons for leaving

Organisation: Work in a small group. You are all people involved in work on the plantation – slaves, overseers, traders, owner and family ...

Situation: Create an incident on the plantation which makes one of the slaves decide to try to escape – for instance, he or she is accused of not working hard enough and is ordered to be sold.

2 Persuasion

Organisation: Work in pairs. Imagine that both of you are slaves on the plantation.

Situation: One of you has decided to escape and tries to persuade the other to go along.

First line: We'll never get a chance like this again.

3 Questions

Organisation: Work in a group of three or four. One of you takes on the role of Miss Emily or another member of the family in the big house. The others are slaves who did not try to escape but who may know something of what has happened.

Situation: Miss Emily wants to get information about the escape. She may try to bribe or threaten the others.

First line: I know that you've always been completely loyal ...

4 Saying goodbye

Organisation: Work in a group of four. One or two of you have
decided to escape. The others are their parents or family
members – perhaps people who are too old or too young to go
along.

Situation: There is only a short time to go before you leave.
Explain to your relations why you have made such a
dangerous decision. They may try to change your mind, or
they may give you help or advice.

First line: There's very little time ...

---

5 On the run

Organisation: Work in a group of five or six. You have left the
plantation on your journey to freedom.

Situation: Create three tableaux, or still pictures, of the most
exciting or difficult or dangerous moments of your journey.
(You might include these tableaux if you are performing the
play.)

---

6 New courage

Organisation: In the play, Linda seems rather spoiled and
selfish. Work in a small group as the runaway slaves.

Situation: Create an incident on the journey which shows Linda
in a different light – perhaps being resourceful and
imaginative, or clever at avoiding capture, or unexpectedly
brave. (You could include this scene also in your
performance of the play.)

---

7 Ambitions

Organisation: In the play, Hedy longs to be able to read and
write. Work with a partner. Imagine that one of you is Hedy
or another young slave in a similar position. Your partner is
a young member of the family in the big house.

Situation: Hedy has found a book and begun to look at it. She is
discovered by the white child, whose attitude to her may be
hostile or friendly.

First line: Why are you touching that book?

---

8   Oral history

Organisation: Work with a partner. One of you is Harriet Tubman, or another of the abolitionists who helped so many people to escape. The other is an interviewer – perhaps an historian or a journalist, or a novelist who wants to write about life during slavery.

Situation: The slaves are free, but it is important that their stories and their lives are remembered. Interview your partner, who may be now a very elderly person. What does he or she remember of the struggle of those days?

First line: Sometimes it seems like only yesterday ...

9   Just the beginning

Organisation: Look again at the last scene of the play. Work in a small group.

Situation: You are ex-slaves who have settled in Canada. Create a scene in which you imagine what life is like for the new arrivals a year after they reach freedom. Share your scene with the rest of the class.

10   Images of courage

Organisation: Work in a small group. Imagine that it is the end of the 20th century. Black people have at last reached true equality and freedom.

Situation: A memorial is to be created to all the slaves who risked so much to gain their freedom, and to all the people who helped them. Discuss in your group what a fitting memorial would be. You might want to set up a statue, create a park or garden, a school or library, endow a scholarship fund, or do something else which will keep alive the memories of courageous people like Harriet Tubman. Share your ideas with the rest of the class. If you decide on a particular image, such as a statue, describe it in detail to the others.

11   Slave stealers

Organisation: Work in a large group – perhaps, the whole class. Your teacher might help you by working in role as an abolitionist. Imagine that you are all ex-slaves who have reached the safety of Canada and made new lives there.

Situation: A message has been sent to you by Harriet Tubman. There is now a large price on her head so she cannot return to the United States to lead more slaves to freedom. She asks whether any of the group are prepared to risk their own freedom to help others who are still in bondage.

First line: We have a very difficult decision to make.

12 Disguises

Organisation: Work in pairs. Each of you creates a new identity for yourself – one which will provide you with a reason for travelling in the the South. Think of a new name and background for yourself.

Situation: You meet in the South. Both of you are travelling with false identities. Talk to each other but be careful not to reveal your real purpose – to free the slaves. Remember that you may not be able to trust everyone you meet, and if you were once a slave yourself, you may be in danger of recapture.

First line: How far are you going?

LIFE
ON THE PLANTATION

Many slave owners in the South had grown very wealthy
through the labour of their slaves. A large plantation, as the big
estates were called, was like a world in itself. There was the
mansion of the slave owner, the 'big house', as it was often
known. For the slaves there was a line of little cabins, scarcely
more than one-room huts, which were made of rough timber
with earth floors. These were called 'Quarters'. There was
very little furniture in the huts; most slaves slept on a blanket
over a pile of straw on the rough floor. The overseer, who was in
charge of the slaves, lived in a house nearby. There were barns
and sheds for the animals, tools and crops. Near the big house

were gardens, and surrounding everything were the fields of cotton and the woods.

There were two kinds of slaves on the plantations – field hands and house servants. Most slaves were field hands who worked in gangs under the supervision of the overseer. Theirs was the heavy work of planting, cultivating and harvesting the crops. Men, women and children were field hands. Apart from growing the crops, they did other jobs, too, like clearing the land, burning the undergrowth, chopping the wood and mending the fences. Poorly clothed and often quite hungry, they were forced to work from sunrise to sunset – and sometimes into the night. If they didn't work hard enough, they were beaten with a lash by the overseer.

The luckier slaves were the house servants. They cooked the meals, did the washing, cared for the house, yard and garden, looked after the children of the owner, drove the carriages ... Some, like Linda in the play, were the personal servants of the owner's family.

The owners and their overseers were often cruel and ruthless. Various laws, the Slave Codes, denied rights to the slaves. They were not allowed to leave the plantation without permission; they could not own property or buy and sell goods; they were not allowed to meet in groups without a white person being present ... They were given almost no protection against the brutality of their owners. For the smallest offences, they would be severely punished – whippings, beatings and brandings were common. If the owners decided to sell them, they might be cut off from their families for years – perhaps for ever. Their lives were harsh and, for most of them, freedom remained a dream.

These extracts were written by ex-slaves. They describe life on the plantations.

The first is by Solomon Northup.

'... they often labour till the middle of the night'

An hour before daylight the horn is blown. Then the slaves arouse, prepare their breakfast, fill a gourd with water, in another deposit their dinner of cold bacon and corn cake, and hurry to the field again. It is an offence, invariably followed by a flogging, to be found at the quarters after daybreak. Then the fears and labours of another day begin and until its close there is no such thing as rest.

... they are not permitted to be a moment idle until it is too dark to see, and when the moon is full they often labour till the middle of the night. They do not dare to stop even at dinner time, nor return to the quarters, however late it be, until the order to halt is given by the driver.

from *To Be a Slave* by Julius Lester

Here Josiah Henson describes the living conditions on the plantations:

'... the rain and snow blew through the cracks'

We lodged in log huts and on the bare ground. Wooden floors were an unknown luxury. In a single room were huddled, like cattle, ten or a dozen persons, men, women and childen. All ideas of refinement and decency were, of course, out of the question. There were neither bedsteads, nor furniture of any description. Our beds were collections of straw and old rags,

thrown down in the corners and boxed in with boards, a single blanket the only covering. Our favourite way of sleeping, however, was on a plank, our heads raised on an old jacket and our feet toasting before the smouldering fire. The wind whistled and the rain and snow blew in through the cracks, and the damp earth soaked in the moisture till the floor was miry as a pigsty. Such were our houses.

The principal food of those upon my master's plantation consisted of cornmeal and salt herrings, to which was added in summer a little buttermilk and a few vegetables which each might raise for himself and his family on the little piece of ground which was assigned to him for the purpose, called a truck patch.

In ordinary times we had two regular meals a day: breakfast at twelve o'clock, after labouring from daylight, and supper when the work of the remainder of the day was over. In harvest season we had three. Our dress was of tow cloth; for the children nothing but a shirt; for the older ones a pair of pantaloons or a gown in addition, according to the sex. Besides these, in the winter a round jacket or overcoat, a wool hat once in two or three years, for the males, and a pair of shoes once a year.

from *To Be a Slave* by Julius Lester

This is part of Frederick Douglass's account:

'... he was a cruel man'

There were no beds given the slaves, unless one coarse blanket be considered such, and none but the men and women had these. This, however, is not considered a very great privation. They find less difficulty from the want of beds, than from the want of time to sleep; for when their day's work in the field is done, the most of them having their washing, mending and cooking to do, and having few or none of the ordinary facilities for doing either of these, very many of their sleeping hours are consumed in preparing for the field the coming day; and when this is done, old and young, male and female, married and single, drop down side by side, on one common bed – the cold, damp floor – each covering himself or herself with their miserable blankets; and here they sleep till they are summoned to the field by the driver's horn. At the sound of this, all must rise, and be off to the field. There must be no halting; everyone must be at his or her post; and woe betides them who hear not this morning summons to the field; for if they are not awakened by the sense of hearing, they are by the sense of feeling: no age nor sex finds any favor. Mr Severe, the overseer, used to stand by the door of the quarter, armed with a large hickory stick and heavy cowskin, ready to whip anyone who was so unfortunate as not to hear, or, from any cause, was prevented from being ready to start for the field at the sound of the horn.

Mr Severe was rightly named: he was a cruel man. I have seen him whip a woman, causing the blood to run half an hour at the time; and this, too, in the midst of her crying children, pleading for their mother's release. He seemed to take pleasure in manifesting his fiendish barbarity.

from *Narrative of the Life of Frederick Douglass*

Read the extracts carefully before working on these activities:

1 Life on the plantation

Organisation: Work in small groups of five or six. Create a
tableau, or still picture, of one aspect of life on the plantation
– perhaps the field hands at work, or the family and their
servants in the big house, or life in the slave quarters. Try to
create a moment which will show, not only what people are
doing in the scene, but will hint at their attitudes and
feelings.

Extension: Each group should show their tableau to the rest of
the class. Members of the class can give a title to each
tableau. They can also choose different people from the
tableaux and ask them to speak their thoughts and feelings
aloud.

Written extension: Each person who has been part of a tableau
writes a brief account of the life of the person they have been
representing.

---

2 A visitor

Organisation: Work with a partner. Imagine that one of you, A,
is a visitor to the plantation. Your partner, B, is a slave
working in the fields.

Situation: A sees B at work, perhaps struggling to complete a
difficult task. A tries to talk to B, who may be unwilling to
say anything in case the overseer sees them.

First line: How long have you been working like this?

---

3 A letter of thanks

Written work: As a visitor to the plantation, write a letter of
thanks to your hosts. Express how grateful you are for their
kindness to you during your stay, but at the same time refer
to your feelings about what you witnessed on the plantation.

---

4 The mansion

Organisation: Work in a group of two or three. All of you are
young slaves who work in the fields.

Situation: One of you has been sent to the big house with a message for one of the family. You have never been close to the house before. Describe the interior of the house and its furniture to your friends. What made the most impression on you?

First line: You'll never believe what I saw ...

5   Back home

Organisation: Work with a partner.

Situation: Imagine that one of you has recently visited a southern plantation. Tell your friend, who lives in the North, what your impressions were. Can you help them to understand what slavery means?

First line: At first I thought it was a wonderful place ...

6   Anti-Slavery Society

Organisation: Work with one or two others. You are people who have travelled in the South and seen the evils of slavery. Some of you may be ex-slaves.

Situation: You have been invited to give a speech to a meeting of the Anti-Slavery Society in one of the northern states. What will you tell them of your experiences in the South? You could share the responsiblity with your partner(s) and each speak on a different aspect of slavery. You could use your friends as witnesses to what you describe.
Share your speeches with the rest of the class.

Extension: If you have access to a tape or video recorder, you might make your own documentary about the history and effects of slavery. You might include some dramatised moments and use your own research as well as the extracts in this book.

POEMS AND SONGS

Southern Mansion

Poplars are standing there still as death
and ghosts of dead men
meet their ladies walking
two by two beneath the shade
and standing on the marble steps.

There is a sound of music echoing
through the open door
and in the field there is
another sound tinkling in the cotton:
chains of bondmen dragging on the ground.

The years go back with an iron clank,
a hand is on the gate,
a dry leaf trembles on the wall.
Ghosts are walking.
They have broken roses down
And poplars stand there still as death.

This poem is by Arna Bontemps, a black writer and academic,
born in the South in 1902, and brought up in California.

Some of the songs sung on the plantation described life as it really was for the slaves:

> *We raise the wheat,*
> *They give us the corn,*
> *We bake the bread,*
> *They give us the crust;*
> *We sift the meal,*
> *They give us the skin,*
> *And that's the way*
> *They take us in.*

> *The big bee flies high,*
> *The little bee makes the honey.*
> *The black folks make the cotton*
> *And the white folks get the money.*

This poem, written by Lewis Allan, and made famous by the blues singer, Billie Holiday, is about the violent deaths of some black people in the South:

Strange Fruit

Southern trees bear a strange fruit,
Blood on the leaves and blood at the root,
Black bodies swinging in the southern breeze,
Strange fruit hanging from the poplar trees.
Pastoral scene of the gallant south,
The bulging eyes and the twisted mouth,
Scent of magnolia, sweet and fresh
Then the sudden smell of burning flesh.
Here is a fruit for the crows to pluck,
For the rain to gather, for the wind to suck,
For the sun to rot, for the trees to drop,
Here is a strange and bitter crop.

Read *Southern Mansion* and *Strange Fruit* carefully. What connections do you notice between them?

1   Images

Organisation: Work in a small group.

Situation: Create two tableaux – one of life in the mansion, and the other of life among the slaves. Use the ideas in the poems and the information in the extracts.
Share your tableaux with the rest of the class.
Bring your tableaux to life, so that you are creating a kind of dance drama. Remember to establish a ghostly feeling by making your movements slow or exaggerated.

2   Strange meeting

Organisation: Work with a partner. One of you is a modern-day visitor to a southern plantation which has been restored for tourists to visit. Your partner is a ghost, either of a slave who worked there, or of one of the plantation owner's family.

Situation: The tourist has wandered away from the rest of the visitors. In a quiet corner of the house or grounds, the ghost appears. What will the ghost tell of the life it used to lead? Does the ghost have a message for the tourist? Can the tourist give the ghost any news of the way the world has changed?

Written extension: *Either* write a poem as if you were one of the ghosts revisiting the plantation, *or* write a ghost story set on the plantation. Try to make your poem or story as mysterious and scary as possible. Make sure, too, that you bring out some of the strong feelings which have remained with the ghosts of the plantation people – for instance, feelings of fear, bitterness, revenge on the part of the slaves and cruelty, greed or guilt on the part of the owner and his family.

c

RESISTANCE

The Africans who were captured and brought as slaves to America found themselves separated from everything that was familiar to them. They were forced to speak American English, but forbidden to learn to read and write. Although they lived without rights in inhuman conditions, no amount of hard work or suffering could limit their imaginations. Out of their memories of Africa and their experiences in the 'New World' came a number of songs and folktales created out of sorrow, courage and resistance.

The People Could Fly

They say the people could fly. Say that long ago in Africa, some of the people knew magic. And they would walk up on the air like climbin up on a gate. And they flew like blackbirds over the fields. Black, shiny wings flappin against the blue up there.

Then, many of the people were captured for Slavery. The ones that could fly shed their wings. They couldn't take their wings across the water on the slave ships. Too crowded, don't you know.

The folks were full of misery, then. Got sick with the up and down of the sea. So they forgot about flyin when they could no longer breathe the sweet scent of Africa.

Say the people who could fly kept their power, although they shed their wings. They kept their secret magic in the land of slavery. They looked the same as the other people from Africa who had been coming over, who had dark skin. Say you couldn't tell anymore one who could fly from one who couldn't.

One such who could was an old man, call him Toby. And standin tall, yet afraid, was a young woman who once had wings. Call her Sarah. Now Sarah carried a babe tied to her back. She trembled to be so hard worked and scorned.

The slaves labored in the fields from sunup to sundown. The owner of the slaves callin himself their Master. Say he was a hard lump of clay. A hard, glinty coal. A hard rock pile, wouldn't be moved. His Overseer on horseback pointed out the slaves who were slowin down. So the one called Driver cracked his whip over the slow ones to make them move faster. That whip was a slice-open cut of pain. So they did move faster. Had to.

Sarah hoed and chopped the row as the babe on her back slept.

Say the child grew hungry. That babe started up bawling too loud. Sarah couldn't stop to feed it. Couldn't stop to soothe and quiet it down. She let it cry. She didn't want to. She had no heart to croon to it.

'Keep that thing quiet,' called the Overseer. He pointed his finger at the babe. The woman scrunched low. The Driver cracked his whip across the babe anyhow. The babe hollered like any hurt child, and the woman fell to the earth.

The old man that was there, Toby, came and helped her to her feet.

'I must go soon,' she told him.

'Soon,' he said.

Sarah couldn't stand up straight any longer. She was too weak. The sun burned her face. The babe cried and cried, 'Pity me, oh, pity me,' say it sounded like. Sarah was so sad and starvin, she sat down in the row.

'Get up, you black cow,' called the Overseer. He pointed his hand, and the Driver's whip snarled around Sarah's legs. Her sack dress tore into rags. Her legs bled onto the earth. She couldn't get up.

Toby was there where there was no one to help her and the babe.

'Now, before it's too late,' panted Sarah. 'Now, Father!'

'Yes, Daughter, the time is come,' Toby answered.

'Go, as you know how to go!'

He raised his arms, holding them out to her. '*Kum ... yali, kum buba tambe*,' and more magic words, said so quickly, they sounded like whispers and sighs.

The young woman lifted one foot on the air. Then the other. She flew clumsily at first, with the child now held tightly in her arms. Then she felt the magic, the African mystery. Say she rose just as free as a bird. As light as a feather.

The Overseer rode after her, hollerin. Sarah flew over the fences. She flew over the woods. Tall trees could not snag her. Nor could the Overseer. She flew like an eagle now, until she was gone from sight. No one dared speak about it. Couldn't believe it. But it was, because they that was there saw that it was.

Say the next day was dead hot in the fields. A young man slave fell from the heat. The Driver come and whipped him. Toby come over and spoke words to the fallen one. The words of ancient Africa are never heard completely. The young man forgot them as soon as he heard them. They went way inside him. He got up and rolled over on the air. He rode it awhile. And he flew away.

Another and another fell from the heat. Toby was there. He cried out to the fallen and reached his arms out to them. '*Kum kunka yali, kum ... tambe!*' Whispers and sighs. And they too rose on the air. They rode the hot breezes. The ones flyin were black and shinin sticks, wheelin above the head of the Overseer. They crossed the rows, the fields, the fences, the streams, and were away.

'Seize the old man!' cried the Overseer. 'I heard him say the magic *words*. Seize him!'

The one callin himself Master come runnin. The Driver got his whip ready to curl around old Toby and tie him up. The slave owner took his hip gun from its place. He meant to kill old, black Toby.

But Toby just laughed. Say he threw back his head and said, 'Hee, hee! Don't you know who I am? Don't you know some of us in this field?' He said it to their faces. 'We are the ones who fly!'

And he sighed the ancient words that were a dark

promise. He said them all around to the others in the field under the whip, '...*buba yali* ...*buba tambe* ....'

There was a great outcryin. The bent backs straighted up. Old and young who were called slaves and could fly joined hands. Say like they would ring-sing. But they didn't shuffle in a circle. They didn't sing. They rose on the air. They flew in a flock that was black against the heavenly blue. Black crows or black shadows. It didn't matter, they went so high. Say they flew away to *Free-dom*.

And the old man, old Toby, flew behind them, takin care of them. He wasn't cryin. He wasn't laughin. He was the seer. His gaze fell on the plantation where the slaves who could not fly waited.

'*Take us with you!*' Their looks spoke it but they were afraid to shout it. Toby couldn't take them with him. Hadn't the time to teach them to fly. They must wait for a chance to run.

'Goodie-bye!' the old man called Toby spoke to them, poor souls! And he was flyin gone.

So they say. The Overseer told it. The one called Master said it was a lie, a trick of the light. The Driver kept his mouth shut.

The slaves who could not fly told about the people who could fly to their children. When they were free. When they sat close before the fire in the free land, they told it. They did so love firelight and *Free-dom*, and tellin.

They say that the children of the ones who could not fly told their children. And now, me, I have told it to you.

The People Could Fly *is one of the most extraordinary, moving tales in black folklore. There are numerous separate accounts of flying Africans and slaves in the black folktale literature. Such accounts are often combined with tales of slaves disappearing.*
The People Could Fly *is a detailed fantasy tale of suffering, of magic power exerted against the so-called Master and his underlings. Finally, it is a powerful testament to the millions of slaves who never had the opportunity to 'fly' away. They remained slaves, as did their children.*
The People Could Fly *was first told and retold by those who had only their imaginations to set them free.*

1 Dreams of freedom

Organisation: Read the story carefully. Work with a partner. Imagine you are both slaves, and you are resting together after your day's work in the fields.

Situation: You have both heard the legend of the people who had the power to fly. One of you has had a dream that you have been given this power. Describe your dream to your partner.

First line: I've had the strangest dream ...

2 Memories

Organisation: Work in a group of two or three. Imagine that one of you is an elderly slave who was in the fields when this strange incident took place. The others are young people.

Situation: Many years have passed since that day, but you remember it clearly. Describe what happened in as much detail as you can. Will the young people believe you?

First line: I'll never forget that day as long as I live.

3 Explanations

Organisation: Work with a partner. Imagine that one of you is an overseer who was in the field that day. Your partner is the plantation owner.

Situation: Try to explain to the owner exactly what happened, and why so many slaves are missing.

First line: I think it was some kind of trick ...

4 The power to fly

Written work: 1 Create a legend which explains why some people were originally given the power to fly. Was it something magic they discovered? Were they given the power in return for something they did?
2 Write a letter from the master to a friend. What explanation will he give for the loss of so many of his slaves?

Discussion: 1 Why were stories like this one so important to the slaves?
2 Can you think of any other stories or legends which might have a similar effect?

ACTS OF RESISTANCE

Many, many slaves fought against slavery, even though there were great dangers involved and they risked severe punishment, including death, if they were caught. There were uprisings and revolts which sent waves of fear and shock through the slave-owning community of the South. There were acts of sabotage – forests, barns and homes were burned – and property was stolen. Some slave owners and overseers were murdered.

Many slaves ran away. In the 1850s, over 1,000 slaves escaped to Canada each year. Sometimes newspapers had several columns of advertisements for 'wanted' runaway slaves.

One ex-slave, Henry Bibb, wrote to his former master:

> You may think hard of us for running from slavery, but as to myself, I have but one apology to make for it, which is this: I have only one regret that I did not start at an earlier period. I might have been free long before I was. But you had it in your power to have kept me there much longer than you did. I think it is very probable that I should have been a toiling slave on your property today, if you had treated me differently. To be compelled to stand by and see you whip and slash my wife without mercy, when I could afford her no protection, not even by offering myself to suffer the lash in her place, was more than I felt it to be the duty of a slave husband to endure, while the way was open to Canada.
>
> My infant child was also frequently flogged by Mrs Gatewood, for crying, until its skin was bruised literally purple. This kind of treatment was what drove me from home and family, to seek a better home for them.
>
> from *Narrative of the Life and Adventures of Henry Bibb, an American Slave*

For the majority of slaves, however, there was no escape. Yet, in spite of the harshness of their lives and their suffering, they hung to their sense of value in themselves, their families and their people.

Serving gal

Many house slaves used their position to gain useful information. One ex-slave, Susan Broaddus, remembered a particular incident:

Was a serving gal for missus. Used to have to stand behind her at the table and reach her the salt and syrup and anything else she called for. Ol' massa would spell out real fast anything he don't want me to know about. One day massa was fit to be tied, he was in such a bad mood. Was ravin' about the crops, and the taxes and the triflin' niggers he got to feed. 'Gonna sell 'em, I swear fo' Christ, I gonna sell 'em,' he says. Then ol' missus asks which ones he gonna sell and tell him quick to spell it. Then he spell out G-A-B-E and R-U-F-U-S. 'Course I stood there without batting an eye and making believe I didn't even hear him, but I was packing them letters up in my head all the time. And soon's I finished dishes I rushed down to my father and say 'em to him just like massa say 'em. Father say quietlike, 'Gabe and Rufus' and told me to go back to the house and say I ain't been out. The next day Gabe and Rufus was gone – they had run away. Massa nearly died. Got to cussin' and ravin' so, he took sick. Missus went to town and told the sheriff, but they could never find those two slaves.

Susan Broaddus gave this account to the Federal Writers' Project which collected and wrote down the experiences of ex-slaves. The Project was as interested in preserving the speech patterns and language of the ex-slaves as it was in gathering information about slavery. Therefore the interviews were taken down word for word.

1   Suspicion

Organisation: Read the extract carefully. Work with a partner. One of you is 'missus', or another member of the family who was present at the meal described by Susan Broaddus. Your partner takes on the role of Susan, or another house slave.

Situation: As a family member, you suspect that Susan has had something to do with the escape of Gabe and Rufus. How could you find out if she can read or spell?

First line: I'd like you to write your name here ...

2   The message

Written work: Imagine that you are Susan, or someone in a similar situation. You need to get an urgent message to another slave who is unable to read or write. Decide on the message you need to send, and experiment with ways of conveying meaning. Could you use objects or pictures as symbols, instead of words?

3   Education

Discussion: Why do you think the slaves were forbidden to learn to read and write? What difference would education have made to the slaves?

FLIGHTS TO FREEDOM

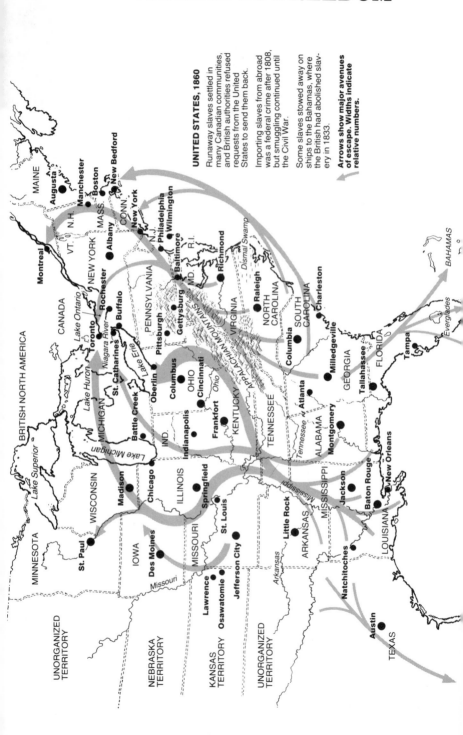

UNITED STATES, 1860

Runaway slaves settled in many Canadian communities, and British authorities refused requests from the United States to send them back.

Importing slaves from abroad was a federal crime after 1808, but smuggling continued until the Civil War.

Some slaves stowed away on ships to the Bahamas, where the British had abolished slavery in 1833.

Arrows show major avenues of escape. Widths indicate relative numbers.

1   Hunter and hunted

Playing this game may help you to understand the anxiety and
tension of being pursued.

You will need some open space for the game. The group should
stand in a large circle. Two people are chosen. One of them
becomes the hunter and the other the hunted. They are both
blindfolded.

Two other people take charge of the two players. They are led
to another part of the circle and turned around three times. The
assistants return to the circle. When there is silence, the game
starts. The hunter must try to find and catch the hunted. This
will only work if the group is silent, so that the tiniest sounds
made by the players can be heard. The rest of the group must try
to protect the players from bumping into objects or moving
through gaps in the circle.

2   Written work

Write a brief log of the journey you take to help the slaves to
freedom. This can be in note form. Try to include some exciting
incidents – perhaps a description of one of the tableaux you may
have seen earlier. Include physical details of the journey – the
weather, the roads you took, the places you found to hide – as
well as your feelings of fear, or panic, or hope.

Wanted

1 Harriet Tubman – Wanted!

Written work: *Either*: devise your own 'Wanted' poster which
offers a reward for the recapture of Harriet Tubman

Or: using the information from this 'Wanted' poster, write a
short news item with the headline 'Slave Stealer Strikes
Again'.

2 The reward

Organisation: Work with a partner.

Situation: Imagine that you are both slaves working on the
plantation. You've just seen the poster about Harriet
Tubman. This amount of money could buy your freedom.
One of you has information about her and is keen to claim
the reward.

First line: I've seen *her*!

Uncle Tom's Cabin

In 1852, Harriet Beecher Stowe wrote a book called *Uncle Tom's Cabin*. When it was first published, it had a great effect on the way many white people regarded slavery. Although later criticised – particularly for the portrayal of some of the black characters – the book won thousands over to the anti-slavery cause.

In this episode, Eliza, a slave who has run away because her child was about to be sold to a slave trader, crosses the frozen Ohio river by jumping on the ice floes. The incident is based on the flight of a real woman who reached safety in this way.

A thousand lives seemed to be concentrated in that one moment to Eliza. Her room opened by a side door to the river. She caught her child, and sprang down the steps towards it. The trader caught a full glimpse of her, just as she was disappearing down the bank; and throwing himself from the horse, and calling loudly on Sam and Andy, he was after her like a hound after a deer. In that dizzy moment her feet to her scarce seemed to touch the ground, and a moment brought her to the water's edge. Right on behind they came; and, nerved with strength such as God gives only to the desperate, with one wild and flying leap, she vaulted sheer over the turbid current by the shore, on to the raft of ice beyond. It was a desperate leap – impossible to anything but madness and despair; and Haley, Sam and Andy instinctively cried out and lifted up their hands as she did it.

The huge green fragment of ice on which she alighted pitched and creaked as her weight came on it, but she stayed there not a moment. With wild cries and desperate energy she leaped to another and still another cake: stumbling, leaping, slipping, springing upwards again! Her shoes are gone – her stockings cut from her feet – while blood marked every step; but she saw nothing, felt nothing, till dimly, as in a dream, she saw the Ohio side, and a man helping her up the bank.

1 Reporting the story

Written work: Imagine that you have either seen or heard of this desperate bid for freedom. Write a headline and a brief news story about the incident for a northern newspaper which opposes slavery.

2 Looking back

Organisation: Work with a partner. One of you is Eliza; the other is her child.

Situation: Many years have passed since you fled to freedom. Your child has grown up safely and knows nothing of the past. What will you now tell about your struggle to escape?

First line: It wasn't always like this ...

SECRET SONGS

Songs were very important to the slaves. Frederick Douglass wrote this about the songs of the slaves:

> I have often been utterly astonished, since I came to the North, to find persons who could speak of the singing, among slaves, as evidence of their contentment and happiness. It is impossible to conceive of a greater mistake. Slaves sing most when they are most unhappy. The songs of the slave represent the sorrows of his heart, and he is relieved by them, only as an aching heart is relieved by its tears.

The songs, or spirituals, which the slaves sang often had double meanings. In the song, 'O Canaan, sweet Canaan, I am bound for the land of Canaan', Canaan was thought of as the North, where the slaves could be free. During the Civil War, slaves began to make up new spirituals which had a bolder message: 'Before I'd be a slave, I'd be buried in my grave, and go home to my Lord and be saved.'

Get on Board, Little Children

Chorus
Get on board, little children,
Get on board, little children,
Get on board, little children,
There's room for many a more.

The Gospel train's a comin',
I hear it just at hand,
I hear the car-wheels rumblin',
And rollin' through the land.

Chorus

I hear the train a-comin',
She's comin' round the curve,
She's loosened all her steam and brakes
And strainin' every nerve.

Chorus

The fare is cheap, and all can go,
The rich and poor are there,
No second-class aboard this train,
No difference in the fare.

Chorus

Go down, Moses

Chorus
Go down, Moses,
Way down in Egypt's land,
Tell old Pharoah,
Let my people go.

When Israel was in Egypt's land
Let my people go,
Oppressed so hard they could not stand,
Let my people go.

Chorus

Thus saith the Lord, bold Moses said,
Let my people go,
If not, I'll smite your first-born dead,
Let my people go.

Chorus

No more shall they in bondage toil,
Let my people go,
If they come out with Egypt's spoil,
Let my people go.

Chorus

O let us all from bondage flee,
Let my people go,
And let us all in Christ be free,
Let my people go.

Chorus

Swing Low

Chorus
Swing low, sweet chariot,
Coming for to carry me home;
Swing low, sweet chariot,
Coming for to carry me home.

I looked over Jordan, and what did I see,
Coming for to carry me home?
A band of angels coming after me,
Coming for to carry me home.

Chorus

If you get there before I do,
Coming for to carry me home;
Tell all my friends I'm coming too,
Coming for to carry me home.

Chorus

I'm sometimes up, I'm
    sometimes down,
Coming for to carry me home;
But still my soul feels heavenly
    bound,
Coming for to carry me home.

Chorus

Read the songs carefully. Make a list of all the references you can find to slavery or to escaping.

1 Secret songs

Organisation: Work in a small group. Read the songs together and practise singing them. Share with each other any other similar songs you are familiar with.

Situation: You have been given a message for some slaves, who are planning to escape but are watched too closely for you to talk to them directly. Can you change the words of a familiar song so that they contain an important message?
Share your song with other groups.

2 Singing for freedom

Written work: Write extra verses to one of these songs, or make up a freedom song of your own.

Discussion: Do you think that songs can be important for people with a cause to fight for? Can you think of any songs that you know which would fit into this category?

HELPING RUNAWAYS

There were many slaves who, though unable to make an attempt to escape themselves, would help others on their way.

Jennie Patterson remembers risking her own safety to help a woman who was on the run:

> I heard a rap – bump! bump! on my door. I answered a-hollerin'! Then someone whispered. 'Hush! Don't say nothin', but let me in!' I let her in. Lawd, that woman was all out of breath and a-begging. 'Can I stay here tonight?' I told her she could, so the woman done sleep right there behind me in my bed all night. I knew she had run away, and I was gonna do my part to help her along. I ... heard the horses and talking in the woods. Dogs just a-barking. I peeped out the window and saw white folks go by. I didn't move, I was so scared they was gonna come in the cabin and search for the po' woman. Next morning she stole out from there and I ain't never seen her no more.

from *The Negro in Virginia*, Federal Writers' Project

1 The search

Organisation: Work in small groups. One of you is a slave like Jennie, who has taken the risk of hiding a runaway. The others are the slave hunters. One of you can be the runaway.

Situation: Instead of passing the cabin, the hunters have knocked on the door. What can you say to stop them coming in?

First line: Open up, in there!

2 Repaying the debt

Organisation: Work with a partner. Many years have passed since this incident. One of you is Jennie; the other is the runaway.

Situation: The runaway has escaped and prospered. Now is the time to repay the debt of gratitude. The ex-slave visits the cabin to repay the person who helped years before.

First line: Do you remember me?

A FUTURE OF FREEDOM

This extract is from an exciting novel about two girls, Julilly and Liza, escaping from slavery. After many adventures, they cross Lake Erie and reach Canada. They are met by Ezra Wilson, himself an escaped slave, who drives them to the town of St Catharines.

On the second morning the leaves on the trees beside their jogging cart were yellow-gold. Ezra Wilson stopped and spread a blanket beneath them and they ate their lunch.

'It's like heaven here,' Liza murmured softly.

Ezra Wilson stood up abruptly.

'No, it isn't heaven,' he said curtly, 'and I've got to tell you how it is.' He looked at the girls a long time and then continued. 'We coloured folk in St Catharines work hard, very hard. But we've got food to eat and most of us have a warm, dry place to live.'

Julilly looked at him with apprehension. What else did he have to tell them to let them know that Canada wasn't just a place with yellow-gold leaves?

Ezra continued to stand. His face was stern but he didn't raise his voice.

'We've found jobs,' he said, 'but none of us can read, and all the white folks can.'

'Read?' Julilly asked, never having thought in all her life that she might ever learn to read.

'It seems, Liza and Julilly, that the white folks don't want us in their schools.' Ezra's face grew sad. 'There's a St Paul's Ward School in St Catharines for the coloureds and a St Paul's Ward School for the whites; and the white school's got more books and more paper and more desks, and a good strong building.'

'But can we go to school and learn to read?' Julilly's eyes grew round with wonder.

'Would they let somebody like me come?' Liza lifted

herself painfully to look into the face of tall Ezra Wilson.

'I'm learnin'.' Ezra smiled down at her and rubbed his grey-flecked hair. 'Now I'll just end all this warnin' talk by saying that salt and potatoes in Canada are better than pund-cake and chickens in a state of worry and suspense in the United States. Now let's eat lunch.'

While he talked, Julilly remembered what Massa Ross had told them a long time ago in Mississippi – that escaping into Canada would be too hard and that living in Canada would be hard, too. But it didn't seem to hurt to remember this. She and Liza could work, and salt and potatoes weren't bad for eating when no slave owner was around to threaten or whip.

from *Underground to Canada* by Barbara Smucker

In Canada

Written work: Write a biography or an obituary of one of the girls in this extract, or of one of the characters in the play. How do they get on in Canada? What obstacles do they encounter? What are their achievements? What will they be remembered for?

DREAMS

The Civil War brought an end to slavery, but not to the injustices suffered by black people in the South. Until the 1960s, the government in the South was in the hands of white people who followed their own prejudices, and practised outright discrimination against black people.

Southern whites claimed that much of what they did was legal. They quoted a court ruling of 1896 which had said that racial discrimination was not unlawful, and that there was nothing wrong in having separate facilities for white and black people, as long as they were equal. So, in the South, there were separate schools, housing, health care, transport ... and lack of funding meant that the facilities for black people were always poorer.

Separate drinking fountains in Oklahoma City, 1939

What happens to a dream deferred?
    Does it dry up
    like a raisin in the sun?
    Or fester like a sore –
    And then run?
Does it stink like rotten meat?
Or crust and sugar over –
like a syrupy sweet?

Maybe it just sags like a heavy load.

Or does it explode?

from *Lennox Avenue Mural* by Langston Hughes

In 1954, a court ruled that separate schools for white and black children were illegal. A blow had been struck at segregation, although many southern states refused to accept the ruling. The following year mass protests against segregation began quite unexpectedly. In Montgomery, Alabama, an elderly black woman, Rosa Parks, decided that she would sit in the part of the bus reserved for whites:

> *Well, in the first place, I had been working all day on the job. I was quite tired after spending a full day working. I handle and work on clothing that white people wear. That didn't come into my mind but this is what I wanted to know: when and how would we ever determine our rights as human beings? It just happened that the driver made a demand and I just didn't feel like obeying his demand. He called a policeman and I was arrested and placed in jail...*

Protests broke out and black people decided to boycott the buses in Montgomery. One of the leaders of the boycott was Martin Luther King, a Baptist Church minister. In 1956, the Supreme Court outlawed segregation on local bus routes – the bus boycott had been successful.

Martin Luther King's movement of protest against segregation and discrimination in the South grew. It was committed to non-violent action – sit-ins, strikes and marches.

For years now we have heard the word 'Wait!' It rings in the ear of every [black person] with piercing familiarity.

Perhaps it is easy for those who have never heard the stinging darts of segregation to say, 'Wait'. But when you have seen vicious mobs lynch your mothers and fathers at will and drown your sisters and brothers at whim; when you have seen hate-filled policemen curse, kick, and even kill your black brothers and sisters; when you see the vast majority of your twenty million black brothers and sisters smothering in an airtight cage of poverty in the midst of an affluent society ... when you are forever fighting a degenerating sense of 'nobodiness' – then you will understand why we find it difficult to wait.

from *The Words of Martin Luther King*, selected by Coretta Scott King

Protests against segregated restaurants

1 Registering to vote

Through various means – threats and bullying, bribery, the introduction of literacy tests for voters, moving vote registration centres away from the areas where most black people lived – black people had been denied the vote in the South. During the 1950s and 1960s, civil rights workers encouraged black people to register to vote. It was not easy. People trying to change things suffered abuse, beatings and death threats; some civil rights workers were murdered in Mississippi.

Discussion: In a small group, talk about why you think it was important for black people to vote in the South. Try to think of the kinds of things they might influence and change if they had the vote. Write down the ideas you come up with on a piece of paper.

Written work: In your group, imagine that you are students from the North who have gone to the South to persuade people to register to vote. Design and write a short leaflet which describes the benefits of voting and encourages people to go to register.
Remember that you are asking people to do something which may be quite dangerous. Your leaflet needs to persuade people to take up their rights, but also to be supportive and honest about the threats involved.

2 A sit-in

During this time, most of the bars and cafés in the South were segregated. In the 1950s, there were many sit-ins by black people at lunch-counters. The white owners would refuse to serve them; the protesters would refuse the move; the café would be forced to close and so lose business.

Improvisation: Work in a group of four. You are students campaigning against segregation in eating-places. Two of you have sat-in at a segregated lunch-counter the previous day. You were arrested and released on bail. Now you meet up with two friends who want to know what happened. Your first line might be: As we walked in, the whole place went quiet.

Written work: Write a diary entry account by one of the students of the sit-in.

In 1963, Martin Luther King's protest movement organised a massive march on Washington. Over 200,000 people joined the March for Jobs and Freedom. In his speech, Martin Luther King described his 'dream' for America.

Martin Luther King speaking to the crowds in Washington, 1963

I say to you today, my friends, that in spite of the difficulties and frustrations of the moment I still have a dream ...
I have a dream that one day this nation will rise up and live out the true meaning of its creed: 'We hold these truths to be self-evident; that all people are created equal.'
I have a dream that one day on the red hills of Georgia the sons of former slaves and the sons of former slave owners will be able to sit down together at the table of brotherhood.
I have a dream that one day even the state of Mississippi, a desert state sweltering with the heat of injustice and oppression, will be transformed into an oasis of freedom and justice.
I have a dream that my four little children will one day live in a nation where they will not be judged by the colour of their skin but by the content of their character...
This is our hope. This is the faith with which I return to the South...
With this faith we will be able to work together, to pray together, to struggle together, knowing that we will be free one day.

The peaceful methods of protest which Martin Luther King used were not supported, however, by all black people. Frustrated and angered by the violence of white society, many young black people felt it was time to strike back – to meet force with force. At the same time, they spoke of their pride in their race, in being black. 'Black Power' became the new slogan. A young black writer, Julius Lester, summed up this different mood amongst many black people:

> Now it is over. America has had chance after chance to show that it really meant 'that all people are endowed with certain inalienable rights' ... Now it is over.

In 1964, the Civil Rights Act made racial discrimination and segregation unlawful. Four years later, Martin Luther King was assassinated.

Many conditions for black people had improved. Freedoms had been won. But racism and prejudice have not been fully overcome and the struggle against prejudice and injustice continues across the world.

> *Out of the huts of history's shame*
> *I rise*
> *Up from the past that's rooted in pain*
> *I rise*
> *I'm a black ocean, leaping and wide,*
> *Welling and swelling I bear in the tide.*
>
> *Leaving behind nights of terror and fear*
> *I rise*
> *Into a daybreak that's wondrously clear*
> *I rise*
> *Bringing the gifts that my ancestors gave,*
> *I am the dream and hope of the slave.*
> *I rise*
> *I rise*
> *I rise.*

from *Still I Rise* by Maya Angelou

A charter for freedom

Martin Luther King had a 'dream' or vision of a better world – a world where all people were treated equally and justly. Read again his speech in Washington in 1963 in which he describes this dream.

Others, too, have had a vision of a better, fairer world. Many of their ideas have been written down as declarations or charters of freedom.

These are some of those ideas:

All human beings are born free and equal
No one shall be held in slavery
No one shall be subjected to torture
All are equal before the law
Everyone has the right to freedom of movement
Everyone has the right to freedom of thought
Everyone has the right to take part in the government of their country

from the Universal Declaration of Human Rights of the United Nations Organisation

The people shall govern!
The people shall share in the country's wealth!
The land shall be shared among those who work it!
All shall be equal before the law!
All shall enjoy equal human rights!
There shall be work and security!
The doors of learning and culture shall be opened!
There shall be houses, security and comfort!
There shall be peace and friendship!

from the Freedom Charter of the African National Congress, South Africa

In a small group, talk about the ideas which *you* feel are important if there are to be justice and freedom in the world. Write down your ideas as statements, like the ones on page 79. These statements can then become your charter of freedom. Illustrate your charter in a way which brings out the meaning of your statements. You could do this with drawings like this, or with pictures cut out from magazines and newspapers.

Everyone has the right to freedom of opinion and expression

Everyone has the right to an adequate standard of living

Drawings taken from the Amnesty pack, Teaching and Learning about Human Rights

Finding out more

About slavery

Information books:
To Be a Slave, Julius Lester (Puffin 1973)
Roots of Racism, Institute of Race Relations (1982)
Slavery, Gary Patrick (Hodder and Stoughton 1990)

Fiction:
The People Could Fly: American Black Folktales, told by
Virginia Hamilton (Walker Books 1986)
Long Journey Home, Julius Lester (Puffin 1973)
Underground to Canada, Barbara Smucker (Puffin 1978)

About black people's lives after abolition

Fiction:
Words by Heart, Ouida Sebestyen (Collins Cascades 1989)
Roll of Thunder, Hear My Cry, Mildred Taylor (Puffin 1980)
Let the Circle Be Unbroken, Mildred Taylor (Puffin 1984)

Autobiography:
Black Boy, Richard Wright (Longman 1970)

About civil rights and Black Power

Information books:
Martin Luther King (Exley 1987)
The Words of Martin Luther King, selected by Coretta Scott
King (Collins Fount 1989)
Being Black: Selections from Soledad Brother and Soul on Ice,
edited by Roxy Harris (New Beacon Books 1981)